Nifast
Safety & Health at Work

Safety & Health at Work

QQI Level 5

Nifast

 **GILL** EDUCATION

Gill Education
Hume Avenue, Park West, Dublin 12
www.gilleducation.ie

Gill Education is an imprint of M.H. Gill & Co.

© Nifast 2015

978 07171 5733 4

Design and print origination by Síofra Murphy
Printed by GraphyCems, Spain

For permission to reproduce photographs, the author and publisher gratefully
acknowledge the following:

© Alamy: 10T, 11BL; © PresenterMedia: 14, 19, 26, 35, 51, 71, 73, 91;
© Shutterstock: 1, 6, 8, 11TL, 10B, 11R, 12, 13, 16, 17, 22, 39, 53, 62,
66, 137, 139, 140, 144, 165, 166; © Wikipedia/Gustavb: 48.

This book is typeset in Helvetica Neue 12/17 pt

*The paper used in this book comes from the wood pulp of
managed forests. For every tree felled, at least one tree is
planted, thereby renewing natural resources.*

A CIP catalogue record for this book is available from the British Library.

Contents

Part 3 Safety in the Work Environment

Part 4 Hazards and Risk Assessments

Part 5 Specific Health and Safety Issues

Introduction

Learning Outcomes

- Analyse the duties of employers and employees as specified in current safety, health and welfare at work legislation.

- Examine the role of the Health and Safety Authority (HSA).

- Explore the role of communication and training in promoting and providing health and safety in the workplace.

- Comment on the elements and functions of the safety statement.

- Summarise the factors which contribute to safe and healthy working environments.

- Outline the principles and procedures of good housekeeping in the workplace.

- Explain the causes, prevention, emergency procedures, reporting and recording of accidents and dangerous occurrences.

- Analyse the causes and prevention of fire-related events, including identification of emergency procedures, the fire triangle and fire equipment.

- Comment on specific hazards and risks when working with equipment, including mechanical and electrical equipment.

- Investigate how personal protective equipment (PPE) is used in the workplace.

- Explore appropriate procedures for use and disposal of hazardous materials and waste in the workplace, including reference to material safety data sheets (MSDS).

- Examine the control and associated risks of a range of health and safety issues, including noise, sound, fumes, dust or any vocationally specific work issue.

- Explain the typical contents of a first aid kit and their appropriate use.

- Examine a range of issues related to infection control, including conditions for the growth and development of micro-organisms, routes of infection, symptoms, ill health, preventive measures and emergency procedures for suspected contamination.

- Investigate risk factors in relation to safety, including hazards, work environments, work practices, effects of medication, drink and drugs.

- Interpret a range of safety signs in the workplace.

- Promote safe and healthy working practices in relation to oneself, others and the workplace.

- Outline risk factors in relation to health, including stress, lifestyle, diet, illness.

- Outline the role of diet and exercise in the promotion of good health.

About these Guidelines

Who Should Read these Guidelines?

This guide is principally aimed at enterprises with a well-defined management structure, where occupational safety and health management can be integrated into the general management system. In large companies, it is aimed in particular at executive directors, boards of directors, other boards of management and senior managers who discharge responsibilities for occupational safety and health, and safety and health professionals. Smaller companies with a less formal management structure can use this guide as appropriate to their needs, and safety representatives should also find it helpful. The book can also be used as a learning resource by learners wishing to complete the QQI (formerly FETAC) Safety and Health at Work module 5N1794.

The Importance of a Safety and Health Management System

There are sound economic reasons for reducing work-related accidents and ill health, as well as ethical and regulatory reasons.

Economic Reasons

Besides reducing costs, effective safety and health management promotes business efficiency. Thousands of work-related accidents resulting in more than three days off work are reported to the HSA each year. Work-related diseases and ill health are more difficult to measure, due to their long latency period, but result in excess of one million days lost at work each year. These accidents and cases of ill health are due to failures and deficiencies in the occupational safety and health management in organisations.

Legal Reasons

The Safety, Health and Welfare at Work Act 2005 requires you to ensure, so far as is reasonably practicable, the safety, health and welfare of your employees and to manage and conduct your work activities in such a way as to ensure their safety, health and welfare. This requires you to be proactive in managing your safety, health and welfare responsibilities and to deal with them in a systematic way. This guide should help organisations to improve their safety and health performance by providing advice on how safety and health should be managed, and in the process help them to comply with their legal requirements.

Moral and Ethical Reasons

The proactive management of safety and health in the workplace helps organisations prevent injuries and ill health at work. This guide will help organisations reduce the personal loss and injury caused as a result of accidents and ill health at work. It should also help individual employees take responsibility for the part they play in maintaining a safe, healthy workplace environment.

How will these Guidelines Help?

This guide aims to give practical advice and recommendations on developing an occupational safety, health and welfare management system for your organisation. The words 'safety and health' are used throughout the document for conciseness and are intended to include the safety, health and welfare of employees and others at work due to work activities.

Part 1

Health and Safety Legislation

Learning Outcomes

At the end of this unit the learner will be able to:

- Analyse the duties of employers and employees as specified in current safety, health and welfare at work legislation

- Examine the role of the Health and Safety Authority
- Promote safe and healthy working practices in relation to oneself, others and the workplace
- Outline the role of diet and exercise in the promotion of good health
- Interpret a range of safety signs in the workplace.

General Note

Safety and health principles are universal, but how much action is needed will depend on the size of the organisation, the hazards presented by its activities, the physical characteristics of the organisation, products or services, and the adequacy of its existing arrangements.

Many of the features of effective safety and health management are analogous to the sound management practices advocated by proponents of quality management, environmental protection and business excellence. Commercially successful companies often also excel at safety and health management, precisely because they apply the same expertise to safety and health as to all other aspects of their operations.

While the quality management of products or services and environmental protection principally protect physical phenomena, safety and health management in the workplace involves protecting people and developing a safety culture among employers and employees. However, there are many similarities between the approaches to safety and health described here and those advocated for effective quality management (ISO 9000 series of standards) and environmental protection (ISO 14000 series).

Organisations that manage safety and health successfully invariably have a *positive safety culture* and active safety consultation programmes in place.

1.1 Employers' Duties

The Safety, Health and Welfare at Work Act 2005 (SHWW 2005) describes the duties of employers and employees in Sections 8, 9, 10, 13, 14, 20, 22 and 26.

Responsibility for safety and health management ultimately rests with the *employer*. This responsibility is normally delegated to executive directors, senior managers, line managers, supervisors and employees. Each person's authority and duties should be clearly defined, documented and communicated to them. The organisational and reporting structure for implementing these duties should be illustrated in an in-house *organisational chart* which should be included in the company's *safety statement*.

In addition, each director on the organisation's board must:

- Ensure that each member's actions and decisions at board level always reinforce the message in the organisation's safety statement

- Prevent a mismatch between individual board members' attitudes, behaviour or decisions and the organisation's safety statement so as not to undermine workers' belief in the importance of maintaining good safety and health standards.

Under Section 8 of the Act the employer has a duty to ensure employees' safety, health and welfare at work as far as is reasonably practicable. In order to prevent workplace injuries and ill health the **employer is required**, among other things, to:

1. Provide and maintain a *safe workplace which* uses safe plant and equipment

2. *Prevent risks* from the use of any article or substance and from exposure to physical agents, noise and vibration

3. *Prevent any improper conduct or behaviour* likely to put the safety, health and welfare of employees at risk

4. *Provide protective clothing* or equipment to employees free of charge if risks can't be removed or adequately controlled by any other means

5. *Avoid potentially dangerous work* involving manual handling, and if it can't be avoided, take precautions to *reduce the risk* of injury

6. Check that the right work *equipment* is provided and is properly used and regularly checked and maintained

7. Provide *instruction and training* to employees on health and safety

8. Appoint a competent person as the organisation's *safety officer*

9. *Report* serious accidents, injuries, diseases and dangerous occurrences to the HSA.

1.2 Employees' Duties

The duties of employees while at work are set out in Section 13 of the Act. These include:

1. To take *reasonable care* to protect the health and safety of themselves and of other people in the workplace

2. *Not to engage in improper behaviour* that will endanger themselves or others

3. *Not* to be under the influence of *intoxicants* in the workplace

4. To undergo any reasonable medical or other *assessment* if asked to do so by the employer

5. To *report any defects* in the place of work or equipment which might be a danger to health and safety

6. To participate in and take note of safety and health *training* offered by their employer

7. To make *proper use* of all machinery, tools, substances, etc. and of all personal protective equipment provided for use at work

8. To *co-operate* with their employer with regard to safety, health and welfare at work.

1.3 The Health and Safety Authority (HSA)

The HSA is the national independent body with responsibility for occupational health and safety. Its role is to ensure health and safety at work and it reports to the Minister for Jobs, Enterprise and Innovation. The HSA has overall responsibility for the administration and enforcement of health and safety at work in Ireland. The HSA monitors compliance with legislation in the workplace and can take enforcement action (which can include immediate closure and shut-down of the business), bring prosecutions and impose severe penalties if workers are deemed to be unsafe.

The HSA outlines its roles as follows:

- to promote and encourage the prevention of accidents and injury to health;

- to encourage activities which promote safety, health and welfare;

- to provide information and advice on these matters;

- to undertake and publish research relevant to safety and health at work;

- to make provision for enforcement of relevant statutory provisions.

1.4 Risk Factors for Personal Health

Stress

Stress is defined as 'wear and tear on the body'; it can have physical, emotional and psychological impacts. Stress can be positive or negative.

- **Positive stress** is what makes us get up in the morning; we feel enthusiastic, bright, ready for a new day and new challenges, with a positive view of life – life is for living.

- **Negative stress** makes us want to stay in bed, sleep longer; we feel overwhelmed by the day's work, already anticipate problems, and have a negative view of life – life just exists.

Lifestyle

A good lifestyle implies a good balance between home, work, social and emotional life. This is sometimes referred to as the 'work–life balance'. A poor lifestyle is when the balance in our lives is out of kilter and we engage too much in one activity at the expense of another. Generally this refers to spending too much time at work, e.g. burning the candle at both ends, worrying about work when we are at home, etc.

Diet

Positive stress and a balanced lifestyle will also include good dietary habits – healthy food with the correct balance of protein, carbohydrates, fats, vitamins and minerals. In modern times, being overweight or obese is commonplace in 'developed' countries, particularly among those with sedentary jobs. Negative stress and a poor lifestyle can make people careless about their diet and they may eat too little or too much.

Illness

Illness can have many causes, for example one's genetic disposition or lifestyle, viruses and the ageing process. Among the more common illnesses cited for absence from work are headaches, sinusitis, eye and ear problems, dental issues, mouth and throat cancers, thyroid problems, hypertension, heart disease, strokes, emphysema, COPD, pneumonia, lung cancer, breast issues, stomach pains, gastric or duodenal ulcers, stomach cancer, hiatus hernia, diarrhoea, constipation, bloating, back pain, colon cancer, urinary tract infections, gynaecological problems, cervical cancer, ovarian cysts/cancer, poor circulation in the legs, varicose veins, etc. Some illnesses are more likely to occur in particular employment sectors.

1.5 Safety Signs in the Workplace

Signs and Notices

Safety notices are short, specific written warnings of hazards in the immediate area or instructions on the standard safe operation of individual machines. Some safety notices can be quite detailed; these generally relate to particular work environments or emergency procedures.

HEALTH AND SAFETY NOTICE
USE OF PILLAR DRILL MACHINE

1. ENSURE YOU WEAR GOGGLES AND GLOVES.

2. CHECK GUARD IS FITTED TO DRILL AND IN PLACE.

3. CHECK SECURITY OF DRILL AND REPORT ANY DAMAGE OR BROKEN PARTS.

4. CHECK YOU KNOW WHERE THE EMERGENCY STOP IS FITTED.

5. ENSURE YOU HAVE NO TIE, LONG HAIR OR LOOSE-FITTING GARMENTS THAT COULD BECOME ENTANGLED IN THE MACHINE.

6. USE CORRECT SPEED FOR WORK BEING CARRIED OUT.

7. ISOLATE MACHINE WHEN FINISHED WITH.

8. CLEAN DOWN ANY RESIDUE LEFT ON MACHINE AND SURROUNDINGS.

9. ENSURE CHUCK KEY IS NOT LEFT IN THE CHUCK WHEN FINISHED USING THE DRILL.

Many **safety signs** are internationally recognised and have no writing on them. These are particularly useful in situations where employees, customers and visitors might not have English as their first language. Below are some commonly recognised workplace warning symbols.

Some Frequently Asked Questions

When must safety signs be used?

Safety signs must be used whenever a hazard or danger cannot be avoided adequately or reduced in another way. Before installing safety signs an employer should examine whether the hazard can be avoided or reduced by collective precautions (precautions that protect everybody) or safer ways of doing the work.

What regulations apply to safety signs?

The Safety Health and Welfare at Work (General Application) Regulations 2007 (Chapter 1 of Part 7: Safety Signs at Places of Work).

What types of safety sign are there?

A safety sign provides information about safety or health and can be a signboard, a colour, acoustic signal, verbal communication, or hand signal.

What is a signboard?

A signboard is a sign that provides information or instruction using a combination of shape, colour and symbols but no words.

What colours and shapes are used on safety signboards?

- Red for prohibition
- Yellow for caution
- Green for positive action
- Blue for mandatory actions
- Discs for prohibitions and instructions
- Triangles for warnings
- Squares and rectangles for emergency and information signs.

Revision Questions

1. List five duties of *employers* under the Safety, Health and Welfare at Work Act 2005.

    a) _____

    b) _____

    c) _____

    d) _____

    e) _____

2. Now list five duties of *employees* under the Safety, Health and Welfare at Work Act 2005.

    a) _____

    b) _____

    c) _____

    d) _____

    e) _____

3. Research some of the hazards and risk factors relevant to your workplace (or a chosen workplace of interest) and identify some safe working practices for this workplace. Much of this information is available at the HSA website, www.hsa.ie/eng/.

    a) Workplace hazards:

    _____

    _____

    _____

    _____

    _____

    b) Safety risk factors:

    _____

    _____

    _____

    _____

    _____

    c) Safe working practices:

    _____

    _____

    _____

    _____

    _____

4. *Group Work*

    Take some time to discuss employees' responsibilities in these areas:

    a) Maintaining good health through diet

    b) Avoiding illnesses

    c) Practising stress management exercises

5. What illnesses would you identify as being particularly likely to occur in specific occupations?

    _____

    _____

    _____

    _____

    _____

6. Identify what each unlabelled safety symbol (1–8) represents.

 **Fig. 1**: _____

 **Fig. 2**: _____

 **Fig. 3:** _____

 **Fig. 4:** _____

 **Fig. 5:** _____

 **Fig. 6:** _____

 **Fig. 7:** _____

 **Fig. 8:** _____

Part 2

Safety Statement, Communication and Training

Learning Outcomes

At the end of this unit the
learner will be able to:

- Explore the role of
  communication and
  training in the promotion
  and provision of health
  and safety in the
  workplace

- Comment on the elements
  and functions of the safety
  statement

- Clearly understand some of the relevant terminology
  used in a health and safety context.

2.1 Training, Awareness and Competence

If employees are to make the maximum contribution to safety and health, adequate arrangements *must* be in place to ensure that they have the necessary skills to do their work safely. This means more than simply training. Experience of applying skills and knowledge is an important ingredient and needs to be gained under adequate supervision. Managers should know the relevant legislation and be able to manage safety and health effectively. All employees need to be able to work in a safe and healthy manner. It is also necessary to check the abilities of contractors where they work close to, or in collaboration with, direct employees.

Good arrangements include:

- Recruitment and placement procedures that ensure employees (including managers) have the necessary physical and mental *abilities to do their job* or can acquire them through training and experience. This may require individual fitness assessments by medical examination and tests of physical fitness or aptitudes and abilities where work-associated risks require it.

- Systems to identify safety and health *training needs* arising from recruitment, changes in staff, plant, substances, technology, processes or work practices.

- Training *documentation* as appropriate to the size and activities of the organisation.

- *Refresher training* to maintain or enhance competence, to include where necessary contractors' employees, self-employed people or temporary workers who are working in the organisation.

- Systems and resources to provide information, instruction, training and supporting *communications*.

- Arrangements to ensure competent *cover for staff absences*, especially for staff with critical safety and health responsibilities.

- General health promotion and *surveillance* schemes that contribute to the maintenance of general health and fitness. This may include assessments of fitness for work, rehabilitation, job adaptation following injury or ill health, or a policy on testing employees for drugs or alcohol abuse.

Supervision

Proper supervision helps to ensure that employees develop and maintain their ability to do the job and it is particularly important for those new to a job or undergoing training. The organisation should identify its training needs and implement a training programme that takes legal requirements on safety and health training into account (Section 10 of the 2005 Act). Records of all training should be maintained.

2.2 Communication

Effective communication about safety and health relies on information coming into the organisation, flowing within the organisation and going out from the organisation.

Information Coming into the Organisation

Good sources of safety and health intelligence are as important in developing safety and health policy and performance as market information is for business development. Organisations should monitor legal developments to ensure continuing compliance with the law, technical developments relevant to risk control and developments in safety and health management practice.

Information Flow within the Organisation

If the safety and health policy is to be understood and consistently implemented, key information should be communicated effectively. Key information includes:

- The meaning and purpose of the policy

- The vision, values and beliefs underlying it

- The commitment of senior management to its implementation

- Plans, standards, procedures and systems relating to implementation and measurement of performance

- Factual information to help secure the involvement and commitment of employees and their safety representatives

- A method of ensuring that workers' concerns, ideas and inputs on safety and health matters are received, considered and responded to

- Comments and ideas for improvement

- Performance reports

- Lessons learned from accidents and other incidents.

Three interrelated methods for information flow – visible behaviour, written communications and face-to-face discussions – can be used to provide an adequate flow of information in all directions throughout the organisation. These methods can be both formal and informal, but they should be consistent, especially if key messages can be communicated by more than one method.

Visible Behaviour

Managers, particularly directors and other senior managers, can communicate powerful messages about the importance and significance of safety and health objectives if they *lead by example*. Equally, they can undermine the development of a positive safety and health culture through negative behaviour. Successful methods of demonstrating commitment include:

- **Regular safety and health tours.** These are not detailed inspections but a way of demonstrating management commitment and interest. They also enable managers to observe examples of good or bad performance. They can be planned to cover the whole site or operation progressively or to focus attention on current priorities in the overall safety effort.

- **Chairing meetings** of the central safety and health committee or other joint consultative body.

- **Active involvement in investigations** of accidents, ill health and incidents.

Written and Electronic Communications

Among the most important written and electronic forms of communication are:

- Written safety and health policy statements

- The organisation's safety statement, showing safety and health roles and responsibilities – this can be in paper or electronic format or both

- The organisation's internal intranet site

- Documented performance standards

- Supporting organisational and risk control information and procedures

- Significant findings from risk assessments

- Records of issues discussed and addressed by the safety consultation process.

Safety and health documentation should be tailored to the organisation's business needs, bearing in mind the requirements of specific legislation. In general, the amount of detail should be proportional to the level of complexity and the hazards and risks in the particular organisation. The greater the risks, the more specific instructions will need to be. In some cases, formal systems may be needed to keep track of key documentation, but material should always be written according to the needs of the user.

Organisations can use *notices, posters, handbills, newsletters, email*, internal *intranet* sites or the *internet* to inform employees about particular issues or about progress in achieving objectives. As organisations develop, electronic means of communicating safety and health documents are used more often, but be careful with overuse of this medium. Noting feedback is one method of ensuring that this method of communication is regularly accessed.

The information might include results of inspections, compliance with standards or the outcome of investigations. Well-directed use of notices, posters or email can support the achievement of specific targets or improve knowledge of particular risks, and is likely to be more effective than general poster campaigns.

Face-to-Face Discussion

Face-to-face discussions support other communication activities and enable employees to make more personal contributions. Tours and formal consultation meetings are options, but others include:

- **Planned meetings** (or team briefings) at which information can be cascaded and pooled. Particular groups of workers can be targeted for safety-critical tasks.

- Putting safety and health issues on the agenda at all **routine management meetings**.

- Monthly or weekly **work group process meetings** at which supervisors can discuss safety and health issues with their teams, remind them of critical risks and precautions, and supplement the organisation's training effort. These also provide opportunities for employees to make their own suggestions (perhaps by brainstorming) for improving safety and health arrangements.

- **Day-to-day communications** from supervisory staff that reinforce the information communicated by other methods.

Information Flow from the Organisation

Organisations may need to pass safety and health information to others. This can include:

- **Accident or ill health** information or letters of compliance to the HSA.

- **Safety** information about articles and substances supplied for use at work to other individuals/organisations.

- **Emergency planning** information to the emergency services.

The format for such information is sometimes specified in, for instance, an accident report form, a data sheet, or a prescribed layout. It may be appropriate to seek professional advice on how to present less formal information so that it can be understood by the audience to whom it is addressed. Special arrangements may also be necessary for maintaining lines of communications whenever emergencies arise.

2.3 Document Control

Employees *must have access* to correct and up-to-date safety and health documents or data. Procedures for controlling all documents required by the safety and health management system, whether in written or electronic format, have to ensure that:

- Safety and health documents are readily accessible, clearly written and readily understood, particularly for workers whose first language is not English

- They are readily identifiable, traceable and their retention times are specified

- Safety and health documents are periodically reviewed, revised as necessary and approved for adequacy by authorised personnel

- Current versions of relevant documents are available at all locations where operations essential to the effective functioning of the system are carried out

- Documents and records required to be retained by law (e.g. scaffolding register, pressure systems or lifting equipment certificates) are kept up to date and available for inspection

- Obsolete documents are promptly removed from all points of issue and points of use or other appropriate measures taken to avoid unintended use

- Obsolete documents retained for legal and/or knowledge preservation purposes are suitably identified.

Safety and Health Management System Records

Procedures for identifying, maintaining and organising safety and health records should be established and maintained. Records should be appropriate to the organisation and its safety and health management system, and they should include training records, safety-critical records, and the results of audits and reviews. Examples of safety and health records include the results of noise measurements, scaffold registers, air quality monitoring results, certification of test and thorough examination of lifting appliances, etc. Safety and health records should be:

- In either electronic or written form, legible and easily understood by those who have to use them

- Identifiable, dated and traceable to the activity

- Stored and maintained so that they are protected against damage, deterioration or loss and are readily retrievable. Their retention times should be established and recorded and comply with legal requirements.

2.4 Safety Statement

Initial Review

The organisation should carry out an initial review of its safety and health management arrangements. This review should compare existing safety and health practice with:

- The requirements of safety and health legislation

- Safety and health guidance in the organisation

- The provisions set out in the organisation's safety statement

- Existing authorities and published safety and health guidance

- Best practice in the organisation's employment sector.

As a minimum, in order to comply with safety and health legislation, the organisation *must*:

- Identify hazards and carry out risk assessments for them

- Prepare and implement the safety statement requirements

- Have in place effective safety consultation and employee participation programmes

- Facilitate the selection of and support the role of the safety representative.

Developing a Workplace Safety and Health Policy

By law, employers are obliged to plan their overall approach to managing safety and health and must commit the necessary resources to implement the plan. As a first step, employers must develop a safety and health policy which should form part of the safety statement. It must be specific to their organisation and be in a written format. The content of the safety and health policy of an organisation should be based on the hazards and risks present in the organisation and should reflect the fact that systematic hazard identification and risk assessments have been undertaken.

As a *minimum*, the policy should contain a commitment that safety and health legislation will be compiled with, and should specify those responsible for implementing the policy at all levels in the organisation, including senior managers, first-line managers, and supervisors. It should also define their safety and health responsibilities. Employees' responsibilities should also be addressed. The safety and health policy should specify the organisation's commitment to ensuring that it will manage and conduct its work activities, as far as is reasonably practicable, so as to be safe for employees and others in its workplace, and that it will not allow improper conduct or behaviour which is likely to put safety and health at risk.

In particular, the policy should specify that *adequate resources* will be provided for critical safety and health issues, including:

- Design, provision and maintenance of a *safe place of work* for all employees

- Safe means of *access* to and egress from each part of the workplace

- Provision and maintenance of any *article, plant, equipment or machinery* for use at work in a safe manner

- Provision of *safe systems of work* that are planned, organised, performed, maintained or adapted so that they are safe, particularly for safety-critical process operations or services

- Performance of *ongoing hazard identification* and risk assessments, and compliance with the general principles of prevention as set out in the legislation

- Provision and maintenance of welfare *facilities and PPE*

- Preparation of *emergency plans* and provision of first-aid training

- *Reporting* of accidents and dangerous occurrences to the HSA and its investigators

- Provision and dissemination of safety and health *information, instruction, training* and *supervision* as required.

- Safety and health consultation, *employee participation* and safety representation programmes

- *Reviewing* and *updating* the safety and health policy to avoid adverse effects on the safety and health of employees from changing processes, procedures, and conditions in the workplace

- Appointing competent *people responsible* for keeping safety and health control systems in place and making them aware of their responsibilities

- Establishing *monitoring* arrangements, including safety and health inspections and audits, which should be used by the employer to ensure ongoing compliance with legal duties, responsibilities and controls

- Development of in-house safety and health *competence*

- Employment of external safety and health *experts* as required

- Use of *standards*, codes of practice, guidelines, or industry practices

- *Co-operation* from employees and disciplinary procedures for non-compliance.

The above list is not exhaustive and the critical safety and health issues that could be covered by the policy will depend on the risks in the organisation. If the above issues are adequately covered elsewhere in the safety statement or in the safety and health management system, they might need only to be referred to in the safety and health policy. Back-up documentation may also be referred to in the policy.

The executive board of directors or equivalent **senior management** of the organisation needs to accept formally the contents in the safety and health policy and publicly acknowledge its collective role in providing safety and health leadership in its organisation by:

- Committing to continuous improvement in safety and health

- Explaining to senior managers and staff the board's expectations and how the organisation will deliver on them

- Ensuring that the safety statement is a living document, is prepared in consultation with workers, is reviewed as conditions change, and is brought to the attention of all workers.

2.5 Health and Safety Terminology

Here is a glossary of terms used in this module.

Accident: An accident arising out of, or in the course of, employment which results in personal injury.

Continuous improvement: The process of enhancing the safety and health management system to achieve improvements in safety and health performance in line with the organisation's safety and health policy.

Contractor: Any individual who undertakes, or any employer or organisation whose employees undertake, work for a fixed or other sum and who supplies the materials and labour (whether their own labour or that of another) to carry out such work, or supplies the labour only.

Employee: Any person who works for an employer under a contract of employment. This contract may be expressed or implied and be oral or in writing. An employee may be employed full time or part time, or in a temporary capacity.

Employer: Any person or organisation by which an employee is employed under a contract of employment. Includes a person under whose direction and control an employee works.

Hazard: A source or situation that has the potential for harm in terms of human injury or ill health, damage to property, damage to the environment, or a combination of these.

Hazard identification: The process of recognising that a hazard exists and defining its characteristics.

Ill health: Includes acute and chronic ill health caused by physical, chemical or biological agents as well as adverse effects on mental health.

Incident: An unplanned event that has the potential to lead to an accident.

Organisation: A company, corporation, firm, enterprise or institution, or part or combination of any of these, whether incorporated or not, public or private, that has its own functions and administration. For organisations with more than one operating unit, a single operating unit may be defined as an organisation.

Risk: The likelihood that a specified undesired event will occur due to the realisation of a hazard by or during work activities, or by the products and services created by work activities. A risk always has two elements: the likelihood that a hazard may occur; and the consequences of the hazardous event. Risk is also determined by the number of people exposed and the frequency of exposure.

Risk assessment: The process of evaluating and ranking the risks to safety and health at work arising from the identification of hazards. It involves estimating the magnitude of risk and deciding whether the risk is acceptable or whether more precautions need to be taken to prevent harm.

Safety and health: Occupational health, safety and welfare in the context of preventing accidents and ill health to employees while at work.

Safety and health management system: The part of the overall management system that includes the organisational structure, planning activities, responsibilities, practices, procedures and resources for developing, implementing, achieving, reviewing and maintaining the occupational safety and health policy.

Safety and health management system audit: A systematic and documented verification process to obtain and evaluate evidence objectively to determine whether an organisation's safety and health management system conforms to the safety and health management system audit criteria set by the organisation, and communication of the results of this process to management.

Safety and health objective: The overall safety and health goal, arising from the safety and health policy, that an organisation sets itself to achieve and which is quantified where practicable.

Safety and health performance: Measurable results of the management system related to an organisation's control of its safety and health aspects, based on its safety and health policy, objectives and targets.

Safety and health policy: An organisation's statement of its intentions and approach in relation to its overall safety and health performance that provides a framework for action and for setting its safety and health objectives and targets.

Safety and health review: The formal evaluation of the safety and health management system.

Safety and health target: Detailed performance requirements, quantified where practicable, and applicable to an entire organisation or its parts, that arises from the safety and health objectives and that needs to be set and met in order to achieve these objectives.

Revision Questions

1. *Group Work*

    Take some time to discuss communication purposes and methods in an organisation. Which method(s) of information flow would best suit the following purposes?

    Purpose   *Type of information flow*

    Reporting an accident to the HSA   _____

    Informing staff of a fire drill   _____

    Training a new employee on a
        specific skill   _____

2. *Group Work*

    Working in pairs, discuss the following and agree on your answers.

    a) What are the four steps an organisation must undertake, at minimum, in order to comply with safety and health legislation?

1. _____
2. _____
3. _____
4. _____

b) Who is responsible for safety and health in an organisation?

_____

_____

_____

c) With respect to the safety policy, list ten specific provisions that must be adequately resourced by the organisation/ employer. (Can you do this without looking back?)

1. _____
2. _____
3. _____
4. _____
5. _____
6. _____
7. _____
8. _____
9. _____
10. _____

d) What does it mean to say that the safety statement is a 'living document'?

_____

_____

_____

Part 3

Safety in the Work Environment

Learning Outcomes

At the end of this unit the learner will be able to:

- Summarise the factors that contribute to safe and healthy working environments

- Outline the principles and procedures of good housekeeping in the workplace

- Explain the causes, prevention, emergency procedures, reporting and recording of accidents and dangerous occurrences

- Analyse the causes and prevention of fire-related events, including identification of emergency procedures, the fire triangle and fire equipment.

3.1 Safe and Healthy Work Environments

The main areas of interest in maintaining a safe work environment concern a collegial ownership of responsibility for safe practices, including an ongoing awareness of possible risks and hazards. Contributory factors can be seen as **proactive** – good housekeeping, recognising and preparing for specific risks and occupational hazards; and **reactive** – responding to, reporting and learning from accidents and critical incidents.

Monitoring and Measurements

The organisation's executive board of directors or other senior management team needs to ensure that it is kept informed of, and alerted to, relevant safety and health risk management issues. It is recommended that boards and other controlling bodies appoint one of their numbers to be a safety and health director. This officer will ensure that other directors are kept informed and that safety and health is actively managed on a daily basis. The board of directors or other senior management team needs to ensure that its safety and health responsibilities are properly discharged by:

- Reviewing its safety and health performance at least annually
- Ensuring that the safety statement reflects current board priorities
- Ensuring that its safety and health management system provides effective monitoring and reporting on safety and health performance or when circumstances change
- Appointing someone at senior management level who has executive responsibility for implementing its safety and health management system

- Ensuring that managers at all levels take their safety and health responsibilities seriously

- Being kept informed about any significant safety and health failures and of the outcome of the investigations into their causes

- Ensuring that safety and health risk management systems are in place and remain effective.

Procedures to monitor, measure and record safety and health performance regularly should be *developed, established and periodically reviewed*. The organisation should measure what it is doing to implement its safety and health policy to assess how effectively it is controlling risks, and how well it is developing a positive safety and health culture. A low accident rate, even over a period of years, is no guarantee that risks are being effectively controlled and that injuries, ill health or loss will not arise in the future. This is particularly true in an organisation where there is a low probability of accidents, but where major hazards are present. Here the historical record can be an unreliable, even deceptive, indicator of safety and health performance.

Like planning, *monitoring* safety and health performance against predetermined plans and standard should be a *line-management responsibility*. Monitoring also reinforces management's commitment to safety and health objectives in general and helps to develop a positive safety and health culture by rewarding positive work done to control risk. Two types of monitoring are required:

1. **Active systems** that monitor the design, development, installation and operation of management arrangements, safety systems and workplace precautions.

2.   **Reactive systems** that monitor accidents, ill health, incidents and other evidence of deficient safety and health performance.

Auditing and Reviewing Performance

Monitoring provides the information to let the organisation review activities and decide how to improve performance. Auditing and performance review are the final steps in the safety and health management *control cycle*. They constitute the 'feedback loop' that enables an organisation to reinforce, maintain and develop its ability to reduce risks to the fullest possible extent and to ensure the continued effectiveness of its safety and health management system. Audits, by the organisation's own staff or outsiders, complement monitoring activities by looking to see if the safety and health management systems are actually achieving the right results. Results from measuring performance should be combined with information from audits to improve the organisation's overall approach to safety and health management.

Audit Protocols

Audit protocols and procedures should be established, documented and maintained and should include the following:

● Allocation of resources

● Personnel requirements, including those of the audit team; auditors should have the appropriate training and skills so that they can assess physical, human and other factors and use procedures as well as documents or records wherever possible. Auditors should be independent of the activity being audited and should be able to access support from a wider range of specialists if necessary

- Methodologies for conducting and documenting the audits, which may include checklists, questionnaires, interviews, measurement and direct observation

- Procedures for reporting audit findings to those responsible to facilitate timely corrective action and improvement

- A system for auditing: tracking the implementation of audit recommendations to include addressing the possible need for changes to safety and health policy, objectives and other elements of the safety and health management system.

Audit Records

The organisation should establish and maintain audit records consistent with the safety and health management system records. Their retention times should be established and should comply with legal requirements.

3.2 Emergency Preparedness and Response

The organisation should establish and maintain procedures for responding to accidents and emergency situation, and to prevent and minimise the safety and health impacts associated with them.

Emergency planning should cover:

- Developing emergency *plans*

- *Testing and rehearsing* these plans and related equipment, including firefighting equipment and fire alarms

- *Training* personnel on what to do in the event of an emergency, particularly those people who have to carry out duties (e.g. firefighting teams, first-aiders)

- *Advising* people working or living near the installation about what they should do in the event of an emergency
- *Familiarising the emergency services* with the facilities at the organisation so that they know what to expect in the event of an emergency.

The **emergency plan** itself should include:

- Details on the installation, availability and testing of suitable warning and alarm systems
- Details of emergency scenarios that might occur, and how to deal with these scenarios
- The emergency procedures in the organisation, including the responsibilities of key personnel, procedures for fire fighting and evacuation of all personnel on site, and first aid requirements
- Details of emergency services (e.g. fire brigade, ambulance services, spill clean-up services) and how to contact these services
- Internal and external communications plan
- Training plans and testing for effectiveness
- Details on the availability of emergency rescue equipment and its maintenance log.

The organisation should periodically test, review and revise its emergency preparedness and response procedures where necessary, in particular after the occurrence of accidents or emergency situations. The plan should dovetail with the safety statement as required by Section 20 of the 2005 Act.

Accident Notification

The Safety, Health and Welfare at Work (General Application) Regulations 1993 (Notification of Accidents and Dangerous Occurrences) requires that certain accidents and dangerous occurrences are reported to the HSA. These include the following categories:

- An accident resulting in the *death* of an employee;

- An accident resulting in the *absence* of an employee for *more than 3 consecutive working* days (not including the day of the accident);

- An accident to any person not at work (e.g. a member of the public) *caused by a work activity* which causes loss of life or requires medical treatment by a medical practitioner; and

- Certain *dangerous occurrences* which have the potential to cause serious injury, whether or not they did cause serious injury.

Dangerous occurrences include:

- Collapse of a crane or other lifting machine

- Explosion of any closed vessel

- Electrical short circuit, explosion or fire which results in stoppage of affected equipment or place of work for more than 24 hours

- Uncontrolled release of 1 tonne or more of flammable substances

- Collapse of scaffolding more than 5 metres in height

- Collapse of a building involving more than 5 tonnes of material or of any floor or wall in a place of work

- Failure of freight containers or a road accident involving a vehicle carrying dangerous substances by road

- Bursting or collapse of pipelines

- Malfunction of breathing apparatus

- Contact with an overhead electric line of over 200 volts

- Bursting of a grinding wheel.

Responsibility for reporting any such accidents/dangerous occurrences to the HSA must be assigned to a specific member of staff. Notification should be done without delay, by telephone or via the internet in the first instance. Reports must be made on the prescribed forms via the internet: IR1 (accidents); or IR3 (dangerous occurrences).

Key Questions

These are key questions for employers on the adequacy of their safety and health organisation:

- Does your executive board of directors or senior management team ensure that all their decisions reflect the safety and health intentions in your safety statement?

- Does your executive board of directors or senior management team recognise the need to involve all staff in issues that affect their safety and health?

- Do your directors and senior managers provide daily safety and health leadership in the organisation?

- Do you have an agreed safety and health policy? Is it written into your safety statement?

- Have you allocated responsibilities for safety and health to specific people? Are they clear on what they have to do and are they held accountable?

- Is safety and health always considered before any new work is started or work equipment bought?

- Did you consult and involve your staff and your safety representatives effectively?

- Have you identified the hazards and assessed the risks to your own staff, to others and to the public in the workplaces you control?

- Do you set standards for the premises, plant, substances, procedures and people you control or the products you produce? Are these standards in place and the risks effectively controlled?

- Do you have an emergency plan to deal with serious or imminent danger, e.g. fires, process deviations, etc.?

- Do your staff have sufficient information about the risks they are exposed to and the preventive measures they must take?

- Do you have the right levels of safety and health expertise? Are your employees properly trained and do they attend the training provided by you?

- Do you need specialist safety and health advice from outside, and if so, have you arranged to obtain it?

- Do all your staff accept their responsibilities under safety and health law?

3.3 Fire-Related Issues

Fire is defined as *'a process of combustion characterised by heat or smoke or flame or any combination of these'*.

The chemical reaction known as fire is referred to as the **triangle of fire** because just as a triangle has three sides, a fire requires three elements. Remove one of these elements and the fire can no longer exist.

- **Fuel:** may be a solid, liquid or gas. Solid: wood, paper, plastic, etc. Liquid: oils, fat, wax, etc. Gas: natural gas, propane, oxygen, etc.

- **Oxygen:** The air we breathe is 21% oxygen and most liquids stop burning if the oxygen is reduced to less than 15%, so a fire needs oxygen in the correct proportion.

- **Heat:** When heat is applied to fuel, combustion takes place in two distinct phases. The first stage is when the fuel is heated to 'ignition temperature', when a flammable vapour is given off; the second stage occurs when the vapour is broken down by the heat and allowed to combine with the oxygen in the air, leading to the ignition of vapour.

Extinguishing a Fire

In order to extinguish a fire it is necessary to break the triangle by removing one of its sides, i.e. fuel, oxygen or heat.

- Fuel is removed by **starvation**. This means removing any combustible materials or shielding them from the fire. For example, fire-breaks in forestry, closing fire doors, moving away non-involved materials, etc.

- Oxygen is removed by **smothering**, or removing or reducing the oxygen content in the air. For example, blanketing with sand, foam or fire blankets, closing doors, introducing inert gas, etc.

- Heat is removed by **cooling**; reducing the temperature of the material to reduce its vapour emission. Water is the medium most commonly used for cooling because of its extraordinary capabilities for absorbing heat. Water will convert to steam at a ratio of 1:1700 – one litre of water will convert to 1700 litres of steam (under perfect conditions).

But it is important to note that water is not appropriate for every type of fire. Fires are classified into six main types, each with its own appropriate extinguishing media.

Class	Fuel type	Extinguishing material/ method
Class A	Organic *solids*	Water
Class B	*Liquids* and liquefiable solids	Water, foam, dry powder, carbon dioxide
	Liquids immiscible (unmixable) with water, e.g. oil	**Not** water
Class C	Gases and liquefied gases	Turn off gas supply
Class D	*Metals* (calcium, magnesium, sodium)	Very specialised materials, which must be kept where such metals are used or stored
Electrical	Now re-classed with Class A *once the power supply is cut off*	
Class F	Cooking *fats* and oils	Special foam that 'saponifies' the oil

Fire Prevention

This is defined as *'precautionary activities aimed at stopping the outbreak of fire, early detection and reducing the losses of life and property should a fire occur. Activities included are education, inspection, enforcement of regulations and reduction of hazards wherever possible.'*

Fire Precautions

Fire precautions are defined as *'the measures taken and the fire protection provided in a building or other fire risk to minimise the risk to occupants, contents and structure from an outbreak of fire'*.

Revision Questions

1.   *Group Work*

Take some time to discuss, then answer the following question:

How can senior management ensure that its health and safety responsibilities are properly discharged?

_____

_____

_____

_____

_____

2.   List the elements in a fire triangle.

_____

3. How can you reduce fire hazards?

    _____

    _____

    _____

4. What firefighting equipment is available to you?

    _____

    _____

    _____

Part 4

Hazards and Risk Assessments

Learning Outcomes

At the end of this unit the learner will be able to:

- Comment on specific hazards and risks when working with equipment, including mechanical and electrical equipment

- Investigate how personal protective equipment (PPE) is used in the workplace

- Explore appropriate procedures for use and disposal of hazardous materials and waste in the workplace, including reference to material safety data sheets (MSDS)

- Investigate risk factors in relation to safety, including hazards, work environments, work practices, effects of medication, drink and drugs

- Outline risk factors in relation to health, including stress, lifestyle, diet and illness.

4.1 General Hazards and Risks

Devising Workplace Precautions

Controlling risks is necessary to comply with the requirements of the 2005 Act and the relevant statutory provisions. There are three basic stages in establishing workplace precautions:

1. **Hazard identification:** identifying hazards that could cause harm.

2. **Risk assessment:** assessing any risk that might arise from identified hazards.

3. **Risk control:** deciding on suitable measures to eliminate or control risk.

This approach applies to the control of both health risks and safety risks. However, health risks present distinctive features, arising from their long latency period, which require a particular approach. The approach underpins legislation aiming to improve the management of safety and health for many work activities, for example in construction the factors might include chemical or biological agents, the workplace, use of work equipment, manual handling (according to the General Application Regulations 2007), noise, etc.

In practice, many decisions at these three stages are simple and straightforward and are taken together. Whenever the identification stage reveals a well-known hazard with a known risk, the methods of control and consequent maintenance may be well tried and tested. For example, stairs present an established risk of slipping, tripping and falling. They require traditional methods of control such as good construction, handrails and non-slip surfaces, along with the need to keep stairs free of obstructions. In other more complex situations, decisions are necessary at each stage. These are outlined below.

Hazard Identification

This is required by Section 19 of the 2005 Act and should form a major part of the safety and health management system. Identifying hazards is an essential first step towards controlling safety and health risks. It should involve a critical appraisal of all activities, taking account of hazards to employees, others affected by the organisation's activities (e.g. visitors, members of the public and contractors), and to those using its products and services. Consideration should be given to hazards arising from both routine and non-routine operations. To ensure a systematic identification of hazards, the organisation could refer to relevant safety and health sources of information, such as:

- Legislation and codes of practice on safety and health, which give practical guidance and include basic minimum requirements

- Safety and health websites, e.g. www.hsa.ie

- Authoritative safety and health guidance

- Relevant European Union and other international safety and health guidance

- Information provided by manufacturers and suppliers of articles and substances used at work

- Relevant national and international standards

- Relevant industry or trade association guidance

- Personal knowledge and experience of managers and employees

- Accident, ill health and incident data from the organisation itself, from other organisations, or from central sources such as representative organisations

- Expert advice and opinion from competent safety and health professionals.

There should be a critical appraisal of all routine and non-routine business activities. People exposed could include not only employees, but members of the public, contractors and users of the organisation's products and services. Employees and safety representatives can make a useful contribution to identifying hazards.

In the simplest cases, hazards can be identified by *observation* and by comparing the circumstances with the relevant information (e.g. single-storey premises do not present any hazards associated with stairs). In more complex cases, it may be necessary to take *measurements*, e.g. air sampling, or to examine the methods of machine operation to identify the presence of hazards from chemicals or machinery. In the most complex or most high-risk cases (e.g. the chemical or pharmaceutical industries), *special techniques and systems* may be needed, such as hazard and operability studies (HAZOPs) and hazard analysis techniques such as event or fault tree analysis. Specialist advice may be needed to choose and apply the most appropriate method.

Risk Assessment

Section 19 of the 2005 Act, and many of the relevant statutory provisions (e.g. the General Application Regulations and the Chemical Agents Regulations), include a general requirement to carry out a **written risk assessment**. Risk assessment is essentially concerned with estimating the *severity and likelihood* of harm arising from identified hazards. Where there is more than one employee or other persons exposed, there is increased risk. Assessing risks to help determine workplace precautions can be *qualitative* or *quantitative*. In the simplest cases, organisations can refer to specific legal limits, e.g. edge protection is required on all working platforms where people are liable to fall from a height.

In more complex situations, organisations may need to make qualitative judgements within a framework set by legal standards and guidance. To assess risks, risk assessors need knowledge of the activities and working practices being undertaken. Here again, the knowledge of employees and safety representatives can be valuable. Risk assessments should be carried out by competent people who are suitably trained. Professional safety and health advice may be needed in some cases, especially when choosing appropriate **quantified risk assessment** (QRA) techniques and interpreting results. QRA is used more extensively with high-risk activities and for major accident hazard sites. Here the issue of acceptability of risk might be relevant.

In order to comply with the law, any improvements considered necessary in the risk assessments must be implemented as soon as possible. The risk assessments must be repeated as required, e.g. on the introduction of new technology, new work procedures or processes. In addition, they may need to be *reviewed* after organisation mergers, takeovers or downsizing.

Risk Control

When risks have been analysed and assessed, risk assessors can make decisions about workplace precautions. All final decisions about risk control methods must take the relevant legal requirements into account, as they establish minimum levels of risk prevention or control. Some of the duties imposed by the 2005 Act and the relevant statutory provisions are absolute. However, the general duties of care in Section 8 of the 2005 Act are qualified by the words, *'so far as is reasonably practical'*. This means that in assessing risk, employers and those who control workplaces to any extent must put in place appropriate preventive or control measures to protect the safety and health of employees and others unless these measures are wholly disproportionate to the elimination of the actual risk involved. In short, if the risk is high, a lot must be done to eliminate or control it. To comply with this requirement, employers should adopt the following **hierarchy of risk control measures**:

- **Elimination or substitution:** a permanent solution that eliminates the hazard altogether or substitutes one that presents a lower risk. This could involve eliminating a hazardous process or substance or changing a toxic substance to a less toxic one.

- **Engineering controls** or safety measures to reduce the risk. These can include using machine guards, isolating or enclosing hazards, local exhaust ventilation, mechanical handling methods or protective barriers.

- **Administrative controls** which reduce or eliminate exposure to a hazard by following to procedures or instructions. They may include supervision, a permit-to-work system and job rotation.

- **Personal protective equipment (PPE):** appropriate training in the use and selection of PPE is an essential element of risk control.

4.2 Mechanical and Electrical Equipment

Machinery

Section 8 of the 2005 Safety, Health and Welfare at Work Act requires employers to ensure that *machinery is designed, provided and maintained* so as to be safe and without risk to health. The use of any machinery should be covered by a *risk assessment* in accordance with Section 19 of the Act.

More specific technical requirements are contained in Chapter 2 of the 2007 Safety, Health and Welfare at Work (General Application) Regulations (S.I.Nos 299/2007 and 732/2007), which deal with the use of work equipment. These Regulations, which put the Use of Work Equipment Directive into national law, also include the requirements for the statutory examination of lifting equipment – which apply not only to employers but also to those who hire out lifting equipment.

The duties on designers and manufacturers of machinery are set out in the Machinery Directive (2006/42/EC) which has been transposed into national law by the 2008 European Communities (Machinery) Regulations (S.I.No.407/2008) (http://ec.europa.eu/enterprise/sectors/mechanical/documents/legislation/machinery/index_en.htm). These regulations apply to completed and partly completed machinery, interchangeable equipment, machine-related safety components, lifting accessories, chains, ropes and webbing, and removable mechanical transmission devices such as power take-off (PTO) shafts. This Directive also applies to the import of non-compliant machinery, including second-hand equipment, into the European Union and makes the importer responsible for bringing the machinery into conformity. The European Commission has produced a detailed guide to the Machinery Directive: http://ec.europa.eu/enterprise/sectors/mechanical/machinery.

The Dangers of Electricity

Working with electricity can be dangerous. Engineers, electricians, and other workers deal with electricity directly, including working on overhead lines, electrical installation and circuit assemblies. Others, such as office workers, farmers, and construction workers work with electricity indirectly and may also be exposed to electrical hazards.

How Electric Current Affects the Body

Electric current affects the body when it flows through it. The basic unit of current is the amp. This is the current which flows through a resistance of 1 ohm (Ω) when a voltage of 1 volt is applied across it. However, currents as low as thousandths of amps (milliamps) can have an adverse effect on the body. The table below gives an illustration of the types of effects various levels of current can have on the body.

Electric Current (1-second contact)	Physiological Effect
1 mA	Threshold of feeling, tingling sensation
5 mA	Accepted as maximum harmless current
10–20 mA	Beginning of sustained muscular contraction ('Can't let go' current)
100–300 mA	Ventricular fibrillation, fatal if continued Respiratory function continues
6 A	Sustained ventricular contraction followed by normal heart rhythm (defibrillation) Temporary respiratory paralysis and possibly burns

Most of us have experienced some form of electric 'shock', where electricity causes our body pain or trauma. If we are fortunate, the extent of that experience is limited to tingles or jolts of pain from static electricity build-up discharging through our bodies. When we are working around electric circuits, capable of delivering high power to loads, electric shock becomes a much more serious issue, and pain is the least significant result of shock. For example, a current of 30 mA can cause the onset of potentially fatal respiratory paralysis. The adverse effect will be directly related to the level of current, the length of time that the body is exposed and the path the current takes through the body.

4.3 Personal Protective Equipment

Personal protective equipment (PPE) is any device or appliance designed to be worn or held by an individual for protection against one or more health and safety hazards. Respiratory protective equipment (RPE) is a particular type of PPE used to protect the wearer against inhalation of hazardous substances in the workplace air.

When must PPE be used?

- The fundamental principle is that PPE should only be used as a last resort.

- The safety and health of employees must first be safeguarded by measures to eliminate workplace risks at source, through technical or organisational means (e.g. by substituting hazardous chemicals) or by providing protection on a collective basis (e.g. providing scaffolding instead of harnesses).

- Collective protective measures for a number of employees in a workplace must have priority over protective measures applying to individual employees.

- If these measures are not sufficient, only then should PPE be used to protect against the hazards that are unavoidable.

Why should PPE only be used as a last resort? PPE has its limitations because:

- PPE protects only the person wearing/using it.

- It is ineffective if not working or fitted properly.

- Theoretical levels of protection are seldom reached in practice.

- The use of PPE always restricts the wearer to some degree.

- The psychological effect of PPE may be such that the individual wearing the PPE feels more protected than he or she actually is.

4.4 Safe Disposal of Hazardous Materials and Wastes

The hazards presented by chemical agents must be clearly identified and information on the hazards and controls must be available for all persons who handle, manufacture or store chemical agents.

CLP/CPL Regulations

There are two sets of Regulations on classification, labelling and packaging that define the safety information that must be provided for chemical products:

- The 'new' CLP (Classification, Labelling and Packaging) Regulations implement the United Nation's Globally Harmonised System (GHS).

- The 'old' CPL (Classification, Packaging and Labelling) Regulations implement a number of EC Directives (which apply in Europe only).

Labelling

A dangerous substance to which the CLP Regulations applies must be labelled. The labelling system is distinct from the UN transport warning labels, and must include the following information:

- Name of the substance

- Name and full address of the person responsible for placing the substance on the market

- A list of hazardous ingredients

- Hazard pictograms (you can see some of these in Part 1; there is more information in Appendix D).

Material Safety Data Sheets (MSDS)

- Safety Data Sheets (SDS) are the primary means of communicating information on the hazards of chemicals and the risks they pose to human health and the environment as well as on measures to control the risks. They are regulated by the REACH (Registration, Evaluation, Authorisation and Restriction of Chemicals) Regulation (EC) No. 1907/2006.

- Article 31 of REACH states that the supplier of a chemical, whether a manufacturer, importer, downstream user, distributor or representative, must provide customers with an SDS complying with REACH if the chemical they supply is hazardous.

- The SDS supplied must be in the language of the country where it is placed on the market and must contain the 16 headings set out in Article 31(6) of the REACH Regulation.

Manufacturers are required to supply users with an SDS which contains specific technical information on the risks connected with the chemical as well as safety data detailing the protective measures advised.

The **MSDS must contain information** under the following 16 headings:

1. Identification of the substance/preparation and of the company/undertaking

2. Hazards identification

3. Composition/information on ingredients

4. Exposure controls/personal protection

5. First aid measures

6. Firefighting measures

7. Accidental release measures

8. Handling and storage

9. Physical and chemical properties

10. Stability and reactivity

11. Toxicological information

12. Ecological information

13. Disposal considerations

14. Transport information

15. Regulatory information

16. Other information

Implementation of Labelling

Transition periods from CPL to CLP:

- Pure substances had until 1 December 2010.

- Mixtures have until 1 June 2015.

- Products already placed on the market (on the shelf or in the warehouse) after these dates will be given a two-year extension so that they will not have to be repackaged or relabelled.

Until 1 June 2015, the labelling of mixtures can follow the format of the existing CPL system (orange symbols) or the new CLP scheme (diamond pictograms). After that date (or two years later if already placed on the market), labels must follow the new CLP Regulations.

4.5 Effects of Medication, Drink and Drugs

Employees have certain duties under the Safety, Health and Welfare at Work Act (touched on briefly in Part 1). An employee (at whatever level within the organisation) must, when at work:

- Take **reasonable care** to protect the safety of themselves and others who might be affected by their acts and omissions

- Ensure that they are **not under the influence of an intoxicant** or in such a state that they might be a danger to themselves or others.

- **Submit to reasonable, appropriate testing**, if reasonably required by the employer. The Act gives scope for Regulations to be made that provide for employees to be required to undergo tests for intoxicants to be carried out by or under the supervision of a registered medical practitioner. Such Regulations are *yet to be developed* and until they are made, an employer may not require such testing, although local agreements may apply. The employer may, however, prevent an employee from working if it is apparent that he or she would be a danger to themselves or others.

- **Notify the employer** or the employer's nominated registered practitioner if they become aware that they are **suffering from any disease** or physical or mental impairment which affects their performance of work activities that could give rise to risks to the safety, health and welfare of persons at work. The duty is on the employee to protect themselves and others.

Over the last 60 years or so, industry first reduced accident rates by improving hardware (effective guards, safer equipment); then by improving employee performance (selection and training, incentives and reward schemes); and then by changing the way it manages and organises, largely by introducing safety management systems (SMS). Each improvement reduced accidents down to a 'plateau' level where further improvement seemed impossible.

Now, most accidents (and other 'business disruptions') stem from employee errors or violations. The next big step change in safety has begun and is based on developing good safety cultures that positively influence human behaviour at work to reduce errors and violations.

Safety culture is not a difficult idea, but it is usually described in terms of concepts such as 'trust', 'values' and 'attitudes'. It can be difficult to describe what these mean, but you can judge whether a company has a good safety culture from what its employees actually do rather than what they say.

Symptoms of poor culture factors can include:

- Widespread, routine procedural violations.

- Failure to comply with the company's own SMS (although either of these can also be due to poor procedure design).

- Management decisions that appear consistently to put production or cost before safety.

What is Safety Culture?

'The safety culture of an organisation is the product of individual and group values, attitudes, perceptions, competencies, and patterns of behaviour that determine the commitment to, and the style and proficiency of, an organisation's health and safety management. Organisations with a positive safety culture are characterised by communications founded on mutual trust, by shared perceptions of the importance of safety and by confidence in the efficiency of preventive measures.'

The key elements of a safety culture are responsibility and commitment, which are a two-way street between management and employees:

Management ⟷ Responsibility

Employees ⟷ Commitment

Also key are control, co-operation, communication and competence.

- **Control:** management control systems

- **Co-operation:** participation, commitment and involvement at all levels

- **Communication:** the effective flow of information in, through and out of the organisation

- **Competence:** the ability of all members of the organisation to perform their tasks efficiently and safely and the ability of management to be aware of their responsibilities to manage health and safety effectively.

4.6 Stress, Lifestyle, Diet and Illness

Stress at Work

There are as many definitions of stress as there are definitions of fatigue, mental health and upset. Stress is a negative feeling associated with both physical and psychological symptoms.

- **Physical** symptoms include increased heartbeat, swiftness of breath, dry mouth, sweaty palms and, in the longer term, digestive upset and cramp.

- **Psychological** symptoms range from heightened emotional states, lack of impulse control, feelings of being overpowered or losing control and fearfulness.

People under stress behave differently. They may be angrier, more confrontational, have less time for others and impose an unrealistic urgency on situations. Other characteristics include fatigue, proneness to upset, withdrawal, self-neglect and depression.

The experience of stress varies from person to person, but the feelings it brings about tend to be similar, regardless of what causes the stress. When we are aware of our feelings, thoughts and behaviours as well as our bodily reactions, we can assess ourselves as either relaxed, under slight pressure which we are coping with, under pressure we are finding challenging but acceptable, or under excessive pressure which is causing us stress.

We all have different levels of coping ability and a different tolerance for stress. There are people, often categorised as 'Type A' personalities, who tolerate relatively high stress levels and thrive on the stimulation and alertness brought about by stress. There are others who have very low tolerance levels and thrive in slow-moving environments with low stimulation and evenly paced work.

Coping skills can be improved through regular training, stress management training and through increasing self-awareness and learning to react quickly when we become stressed.

- We may need to take more exercise, relax more frequently, alter our social habits, alter the way we view things, change the work system in some way or re-engineer our world so as to reduce our exposure to the cause of the stress. In short, we may need to consciously **alter our lifestyle**.

- The occupational health approach is to **reduce the stress**, initially from the source, then cut down the person–stressor interaction, and, finally, give protection to the exposed person, when they are exposed. This approach usually involves the individual, the department or section in which the individual works and the organisation as a whole, so that general and specific stressors are reduced or eliminated.

Many aspects of personal, family and work life can cause stress – there are pressures embedded in all these areas of our lives. The Work Positive Programme is an assessment of employees' perception of the stressors they recognise at work. Numerous factors at work can lead to potential stress and diminish our emotional and physical well-being if we are unsupported. These aspects of the workplace are labelled **psychosocial hazards** in some health and safety models, because they threaten mental health in the same way as physical hazards threaten the physical safety and health of employees.

Social support helps ameliorate stress. In stressful environments where support is available and accessed, the perception of the stressor and the resultant stress will be reduced. Social support means having people around you at work who you feel will be there to assist or to listen to your concerns. Common workplace stressors are bullying and the threat of violence.

Revision Questions

1. *Group Work*

    Discuss these questions, then write the answers.

    a) What are the three basic stages in establishing workplace safety?

1. _____

2. _____

3. _____

b) What are CLP regulations, and what is the significance of December 2010 in relation to them?

_____

_____

2. Think of a situation that you consider moderately stressful.

a) What makes it stressful to you?

_____

_____

b) What can you do to reduce stress in this situation?

_____

_____

c) Will your answer to b) reduce the source of stress, or change your reaction to the stress?

_____

_____

d) What can you do in the long term to reduce the stress you feel?

_____

_____

Part 5

Specific Health and Safety Issues

Learning Outcomes

At the end of this unit the learner will be able to:

- Examine the control and associated risks of a range of health and safety issues, including noise, sound, fumes, dust or any vocationally specific work issue

- Explain the typical contents of a first aid kit and their appropriate use

- Examine a range of issues related to infection control, including conditions for the growth and development of micro-organisms, routes of infection, symptoms, ill-health, preventive measures and emergency procedures for suspected contamination

5.1 Noise and Sound

It has been known for centuries that exposure to high levels of noise for prolonged periods of time can result in hearing damage. But little was done until recent times to keep workers' exposure to noise at safe levels. Today, noise is one of the most important occupational hygiene hazards in industry (noise-induced hearing loss has been recognised by the World Health Organisation as 'the most prevalent, irreversible industrial disease') and this has been recognised by implementing specific noise legislation.

Sound is generated when mechanical vibrations pass their energy to the surrounding air. The sound waves then spread out. When they reach your ears, they are converted back into mechanical vibrations, which the ear detects.

Sound Pressure Level and Decibels

Sound pressure level (SPL) is the instantaneous pressure of a noise exerted on the ear. This is the pressure that is detected and measured by microphones. For practical purposes it is equivalent to sound intensity.

There is a very wide range of pressures and so to simplify things and to make the figures more manageable, noise is measured on the **decibel scale**. The decibel scale compares the actual sound pressure with a reference sound pressure (threshold of hearing) using a logarithmic scale.

The decibel measurement is given as dB, and the threshold of human hearing is 0dB and the pain threshold is 140dB.

The table shows some typical noise levels.

Description	Pressure (Pa)	Decibels (dB)
Threshold of hearing	0.00002	0
Quiet office	0.002	40
Ringing alarm clock at 1m	0.2	80
Ship's engine room	20	120
Jet engine at 25m	200	140

Because the decibel scale is logarithmic, small increases in the decibel value actually represent significant increases in pressure:

- An increase of 10dB would indicate a 10-fold increase in loudness. It also represents a 10-fold increase in energy and would be 10 times more likely to cause hearing damage.

- A 3dB increase is twice as loud, double the energy and twice as damaging.

10 dB increase = 10 times louder

3 dB increase = twice as loud

Methods of Noise Control

In any situation where there is unwanted sound, there will be a source producing the noise, a receiver (someone to hear the noise) and a transmission path between the two.

The most effective way of dealing with unwanted noise is to tackle it at source. If this is not possible, attempts to reduce the noise along the transmission path should be attempted. The final option is to deal with the noise at the receiver.

Noise control methods:

1. Controlling noise at source
2. Reducing transmission
3. PPE.

Workers have a duty under the Safety, Health and Welfare at Work Act 2005 to co-operate with their employer and this includes complying with instructions on PPE. When appropriate, employees *must* wear the ear muffs provided. Remember, it doesn't matter how good the hearing protection is if it is left in the locker!

5.2 Dust and Fumes

Hardwood or softwood dusts generated during work processes can be hazardous to health. Certain machines, e.g. sanding machines, can generate particularly high levels of dust. Woodworking can also involve other substances used in processing, which may form aerosols and/or vapours which could include preservatives, adhesives or surface coatings containing formaldehyde, solvents or heavy metals such as arsenic.

Routes of Exposure

Workers can become exposed to timber dusts or chemicals through various routes, the most common being inhalation of a dust, aerosol, vapour or mist. Finer dust generally presents a greater risk since it can penetrate further into the lungs. Skin contact can occur through the eyes, nose or by absorption into the skin.

Occupational Exposure Limit

The occupational exposure limit value (OELV) for both hardwood and softwood dusts is 5mg/m^3 (8 hour time-weighted average). This is set down in the HSA Chemical Agents Code of Practice. Employers must reduce their employees' exposure as far as is reasonably practicable and must not exceed the OELV.

Health Effects

Several potential health effects are associated with exposure to hardwoods and softwoods, for example:

- Irritation or inflammation of the respiratory tract (e.g. rhinitis or runny nose, sneezing), asthma or cancer (particularly sino-nasal)

- Allergic reactions and irritation can lead to dermatitis from exposure to fine wood dust of certain species.

Recommended Control Measures

It is the employer's responsibility to assess the risks and level of protection necessary in the workplace. Various different levels of protection may be required depending on the scenario. The following precautions could be taken:

- No consumption of food or drink where work is being carried out

- Do not launder any protective clothing or PPE at home

- Engineering control measures such as automating timber treatment processes

- Good personal hygiene

- Separate storage areas to prevent the contamination of regular clothing by work clothing

- The work environment should be well ventilated; dust control equipment, such as local exhaust ventilation (LEV), should be used for effective control of dust at source

- Use a suitable vacuum system/cleaner to clear up dust regularly

- Respiratory Protective Equipment (RPE) should have at least a P2 particulate filter fitted to a half- or full-face mask to provide effective protection and should be CE marked; particulate respirators will give no protection against gases and vapours so a combination filter is needed where these substances are involved

- Any RPE worn should be properly fit tested.

Health Advice

Preventive measures include:

- Making respiratory health screening available for all relevant employees

- If an employee has persistent symptoms they should seek medical advice and report the problem to their employer

- Making skin checks available for symptoms of dermatitis these checks should be carried out by an appropriately trained person.

Further Information

- The HSA's website, www.hsa.ie (search for 'chemical agents')

- Contact the HSA at wcu@hsa.ie or LoCall 1890 289 389.

5.3 Specific Work-Related Health Threats

Vibration

Vibration-related illnesses have resulted in large claims against companies in recent years. In March 1999, the UK Department of Trade and Industry in the United Kingdom paid out £500 million for vibration white finger (VWF) to 40,000 former British Coal miners. The average compensation payment for each miner was approximately £6,000.

Vibration is mechanical energy transmitted to the body by direct contact. It is usually considered as two types:

- **Hand–arm vibration (HAV):** vibration transmitted to the hands and arms while holding equipment such as power tools.

- **Whole-body vibration (WBV):** transmitted to the body through the feet or seat.

The effect on the body following exposure to vibration will depend on:

- **Duration of exposure:** longer exposure times will result in greater damage than short exposures.

- **Magnitude of vibration:** exposure to high levels of vibration will cause greater damage than exposure to low levels of vibration.

- **Frequency:** certain parts of the body are particularly susceptible to specific frequencies (e.g. abdominal mass 4–8Hz, hand 30–50Hz, arm 5–10Hz, eyeball 20–90Hz).

Whole-Body Vibration

Whole-body vibration is transmitted to the body through supporting surfaces, for instance floors and seats. Workers affected by whole-body vibration include vehicle drivers (buses, lorries, tractors and other agricultural vehicles, excavators, loaders and other construction vehicles), helicopter pilots and sailors.

The main effects of long-term exposure to whole-body vibration include:

- **Spinal column disease:** the back is particularly sensitive to the 4–12Hz vibration range.

- **Digestive system disorders:** resonance movement of the stomach occurs between 4Hz and 5Hz.

- **Disorders of the cardiovascular system:** heart rate, oxygen intake and respiratory rate can all be increased by prolonged exposure to whole-body vibration frequencies below 20Hz.

Note that the occupations mostly affected by whole-body vibration are sedentary. Workers in these occupations are more prone to these effects because of the sedentary nature of the work.

Short-term exposure to whole-body vibration at frequencies of 0.125–0.25Hz can induce motion sickness (nausea, dizziness, vomiting, etc.). Such frequencies are characteristic of boats or ships on the water (i.e. sea sickness).

Hand–Arm Vibration

Hand–arm vibration typically affects the users of hand-held power tools such as chainsaws, road breakers, hammer drills, grinders, sanders, etc. The vibration is transmitted to the hands, where it causes damage to the blood vessels, nerves, tendons, muscles, bones and joints of the hands, wrists and forearms. Individuals with poor circulation and smokers are more susceptible to this damage.

The effects are collectively known as hand–arm vibration syndrome (HAVS) and typically present as:

- tingling and numbness in the hands and fingers

- loss of sensation in the hands and fingers

- loss of grip strength

- blanching – the tips of the fingers appear white (often referred to as vibration white finger (VWF).

Vibration white finger is similar in appearance to Reynaud's syndrome, which is a circulatory problem. It starts with the tips of fingers turning white on cold winter mornings (when the body's metabolic activity is at its lowest). Gradually, this blanching becomes more frequent and affects larger areas of the fingers. The colour returns to the fingers when the hands are warmed, but the re-warming is often painful, and the fingers go bright red as blood flow increases.

Workers suffering from HAVS often also have some degree of hearing damage because they have been using power tools extensively.

Legislation

The Safety, Health and Welfare at Work Act 2005 places a general legal duty on employers to ensure, as far as is reasonably practicable, the safety, health and welfare at work of all their employees; so, as with noise, employers have a legal duty to prevent employees being exposed to excessive vibration levels, which could result in for example, vibration white finger.

More specific legal duties relating to vibration in the workplace are contained in the Control of Vibration at Work Regulations – Part 5, Chapter 2 of the Safety, Health and Welfare at Work (General Application) Regulations 2007.

Thermal Environment

Extremes of Temperature

Under normal conditions humans' core body temperature is maintained at 37°C ± 2°C. The human body has a number of automatic responses to regulate its core body temperature.

The progressive response and symptoms due to **extreme heat** include:

- An increased blood flow from the core of the body to the surface, causing us to look flushed. The body can then lose heat from the skin to the surroundings.

- We start to sweat and the evaporating sweat cools us down. Excessive sweating may lead to dehydration and cramps due to salt depletion.

- Fainting due to reduced blood pressure to the brain.

- If the core body temperature exceeds 40°C, heat stroke is possible. Sweating stops and mental function is disturbed.

- Ultimately, and in extreme cases, death.

In **extreme cold** the progressive reflexes and symptoms include:

- Reduced blood flow to the skin – causing us to look 'blue'.

- The hairs on the skin become erect – goose bumps. The air surrounding the erect hairs becomes a thermal barrier to the cold.

- We start to shiver – involuntary muscle spasms. As the muscles are working they generate heat.

- If the core body temperature goes below 35°C, hypothermia may set in. This is characterised by listlessness, confusion, disorientation, amnesia.

- Consciousness is lost below 33°C.

- Ultimately, and in extreme cases, death.

Extreme heat is likely in workplaces such as foundries, glassworks and for those working outdoors during the summer. Controls to ensure that these workers are not affected by the extreme temperatures include providing adequate ventilation; limiting exposure time; providing heat-resistant, reflective clothing; making cool drinks available.

Extreme cold is a problem for workers in freezers and cold rooms and for those working outdoors in the winter. Precautions to protect these workers include providing thermal clothing (hat, gloves, jacket, etc.); ensuring that they are kept dry; limiting exposure time; and making warm drinks available (tea and coffee should be avoided as they are diuretics).

Office Comfort

Temperature and humidity are two factors which greatly influence office comfort. Both are also suspected to be major factors in **sick building syndrome**.

Temperature

Office temperature probably generates more complaints than any other area of workplace comfort. Extremes, both hot and cold, cause discomfort. Working in conditions that are too warm will leave employees feeling lethargic.

There is no absolute temperature range given in the health and safety legislation:

- The Workplace Regulations (Part 2, Chapter 1 of the Safety Health and Welfare at Work (General Application) Regulations 2007) specify a **minimum of 17.5°C** for sedentary office work (to be achieved and maintained after the first hour's work).

- The Chartered Institute of Building Services Engineers (CIBSE Guide, Section A1 (Environmental Criteria for Design) states that most people will be neither warm nor cool in rooms where the temperature is **between 19°C and 23°C**.

Humidity

Employees working in environments where the humidity is low (the air is dry) commonly report sore eyes, itchy or dry skin and a stuffy nose. A higher incidence of sore throats and flu-like symptoms may be noticed as dry atmospheres remove the protective film of moisture from the lungs, nose and throat.

There are no absolute limits for humidity, however:

- Guidance in the Display Screen Equipment Regulations (Part 2, Chapter 5 of the Safety Health and Welfare at Work (General Application) Regulations 2007), states that the humidity of the air should **not fall below 30%** in rooms where visual display units (VDUs) are used.

- The CIBSE Guide states that relative humidity should be **between 40% and 70%** to maintain appropriate levels of comfort.

5.4 First Aid Kit

What should be in a first aid box? The table below shows the recommended contents of first aid boxes and travel kits.

First Aid Kit Contents			
Materials	*1–10 people*	*11–25 people*	*26–50 people*[1]
Adhesive plasters	20	20	20
Sterile eye pads (no. 16) (bandage attached)	2	2	4
Individually wrapped triangular bandages	2	6	6
Safety pins	6	6	6
Individually wrapped sterile unmedicated wound dressings medium (no. 8) (10 x 8cm)	2	2	4

Individually wrapped sterile unmedicated wound dressings large (no. 9) (13 x 9cm)	2	6	8
Individually wrapped sterile unmedicated wound dressings extra large (no. 3) (28 x 17.5cm)	2	3	4
Individually wrapped disinfectant wipes	10	20	40
Paramedic shears	1	1	1
Examination gloves (pairs)	5	10	10
Sterile water (where there is no clear running water)[2]	1 x 500ml	2 x 500ml	2 x 500ml
Pocket face mask	1	1	1
Water-based burns dressing small (10 x 10cm)[3]	1	1	1
Water-based burns dressing large[3]	1	1	1
Crepe bandage (7cm)	1	2	3

Notes

[1] Where more than 50 persons are employed, pro-rata provision should be made.

[2] Where mains tap water is not readily available for eye irrigation, sterile water or sterile normal saline (0.9%) in sealed disposable containers should be provided. Each container should hold at least 20ml and should be discarded once the seal is broken. Eye baths/eye cups/refillable containers should not be used for eye irrigation due to the risk of cross infection. The container should be CE marked.

[3] Where mains tap water is not readily available for cooling the burnt area.

Some Frequently Asked First Aid Questions

1. **Is there some flexibility on the contents of boxes and kits?**

   The above table is a general guide on the recommended contents of occupational first aid boxes and kits based on numbers employed. Amounts in the table are minimum numbers and can be increased. The requirements for sterile water and water-based burns dressings (notes 2 and 3) only apply where a supply of clean tap water is not available. A single pair of paramedic shears and one pocket face mask is considered adequate.

   Occasionally the amounts indicated in the table will be insufficient and the actual amounts required should be based on a risk assessment. For example, drivers of dangerous goods vehicles would require more bottles of sterile water for eye irrigation in their travel kits due to the risk of contact with hazardous chemicals.

2. **What first aid records and documentation need to be kept?**

   The names of occupational first aiders must be recorded in the safety statement, along with the location of the first aid rooms, equipment and facilities.

   Written records of the dates of all first aid training, including refresher training, should be kept at the workplace and be made available on request to the health and safety inspector.

   Records of all cases treated by the first aider should be kept in a suitable secure place, respecting their confidential nature, and be made available on request to the health and safety inspector.

The details to be recorded are:

- Name of patient
- Type of injury
- Treatment given
- Name of occupational first aider
- Date

3. **Can a first aider give out painkillers/headache tablets?**

   First aid does not cover the administration of drugs or medication and they should not be kept in the workplace first aid box or kit. In certain circumstances first aiders can administer aspirin, if available, for suspected cardiac chest pain.

5.5 Infection Prevention and Control Measures

What is an Infection?

An infection is an invasion of harmful micro-organisms into the body resulting in illness and disease. Transmission of micro-organisms can be through the faecal-oral route, via vehicles (e.g. equipment), droplets, non-human carriers, blood and bodily fluids, and through the air.

When micro-organisms enter the body they will grow and multiply, and signs and symptoms of infection will become apparent. In order for infection to occur a series of events, known as the **chain of infection**, must happen. There are six links in the chain of infection (pathogen, reservoir, exit point, means of transmission, entry point, new host) and each link must connect for an infection to occur. In the healthcare environment the aim is to break the chain of infection and prevent infection occurring.

Standard Precautions

Standard precautions are a set of general infection control guidelines to be used by all staff who have the reasonable possibility of coming into contact with infection. They provide a foundation for infection prevention and control practices and include:

- Hand washing
- Waste management and decontamination
- Respiratory hygiene and cough etiquette
- Appropriate use of PPE.

Standard precautions aim to ensure that the chain of infection is broken and to prevent the transmission of common infectious agents. Standard precautions assume that infectious agents could be present in a person's blood, body fluids, secretions, excretions, non-intact skin and mucous membranes.

Transmission-based Precautions

Transmission-based precautions are to be used where some transmissible infectious agents require additional controls. They are to be used in addition to standard precautions.

Transmission-based precautions include:

- contact precautions
- airborne precautions
- droplet precautions.

Contact Precautions

Contact precautions should be applied in addition to standard precautions to prevent transmission of highly transmissible organisms that are transmitted from person to person via the contact route (e.g. *Clostridium difficile – C. diff*).

Contact precautions take into account both direct and indirect contact (via a vehicle) or contact through vectors. The following controls should be put in place:

- Isolation unit/room if available
- If unavailable, contact the infection prevention and control manager in charge.
- PPE: gown and gloves for all interactions
- Care of infected person/equipment
- Decontamination of equipment and the environment
- Hand hygiene.

(Strategy for the Control of Antimicrobial Resistance in Ireland (SARI) 2005)

Airborne Precautions

Airborne precautions should be applied, in addition to standard precautions, to prevent the transfer of highly transmissible organisms that are carried via the air from one person to another (e.g. tuberculosis) (Health Protection Surveillance Centre (HPSC) Press Release 2007). Airborne precautions prevent transmission of infectious agents that remain infectious over long distances when suspended in the air, e.g. tuberculosis, measles, chicken pox.

Airborne precautions include using appropriate face masks as per local policy, and staff training.

Droplet Precautions

Droplet precautions should be applied, in addition to standard precautions, to prevent transmission of highly transmissible organisms that are transmitted via respiratory secretions from one person to another (e.g. influenza) (HPSC, 2007).

Droplet precautions are intended to prevent transmission of pathogens spread through close respiratory or mucous membrane secretions. Controls include wearing a surgical mask if within three feet of the infected person.

Revision Questions

1.   *Group Work*

     Discuss the responsibility for employee health, as it is shared in an organisation, when there are noise or dust hazards.

     a) Employer's responsibility:

     _____

     _____

   b) Employee's responsibility:

   _____

   _____

2. List ten items that should be in a first aid box.

   a) _____   b) _____

   c) _____   d) _____

   e) _____   f) _____

   g) _____   h) _____

   i) _____   j) _____

3. What are the two main causes of 'sick building syndrome'?

   _____

   _____

4. What are the main symptoms of over-exposure to vibrations in the workplace?

   _____

   _____

5. Research some methods of noise control. Which method would be best (if money were no object) on a car manufacturing factory floor?

   _____

Appendix A

Measuring Safety and Health Performance

Performance measurement is an essential part of the safety and health management system. Key purposes of performance measurements are to:

- Determine whether safety and health policies and plans have been implemented and achieved

- Check that risk control measures have been implemented and are effective

- Learn from safety and health management system failures, including hazardous events (accidents, near misses and cases of ill health)

- Promote better implementation of plans and risk controls by providing feedback to all parties

- Provide information that can be used to review and, where necessary, improve aspects of a safety and health management system.

Active and Reactive Monitoring

It is often necessary to use both active and reactive monitoring data to determine whether objectives have been achieved. An organisation's performance management system should incorporate both active and reactive monitoring. Active monitoring should be used to check compliance with the organisation's safety and health activities, for example to confirm that recently appointed staff have attended an induction course. Reactive monitoring should be used to investigate, analyse and record safety and health management system failures, including accidents, near misses and cases of ill health.

Measurement Techniques

Methods that can be used to measure safety and health performance include:

- **Systematic workplace inspections** or safety tours using checklists
- **Inspections** of specific machinery and plant to check that safety-related parts are fitted and in good condition
- **Safety sampling:** examining specific aspects of safety and health
- **Environmental sampling:** measuring exposure to chemical, biological or physical agents (e.g. noise, chemical fumes, dusts, X-rays) and comparing with recognised standards
- **Behaviour sampling:** assessing employees' behaviour to identify unsafe work practices that might require correction
- **Analysis** of documentation and records
- **Benchmarking** against good safety and health practices in other organisations.

Inspection

A system for inspecting workplace precautions is important in any active monitoring programme. It can form part of the arrangements for the preventive maintenance of plant and equipment, which may also be covered by legal requirements. Equipment in this category includes pressure vessels, lifts, cranes, chains, ropes, lifting tackle, scaffolds, trench supports and local exhaust ventilation. But inspections should include other workplace precautions, such as those covering the use of premises, other places of work and systems of work.

A suitable programme should take all risks into account but should be properly targeted. For example, low risks might be dealt with by general inspections every month or two, covering a wide range of workplace precautions such as the condition of premises, floors, passages, stairs, lighting, welfare facilities and first aid. Higher risks need more frequent and detailed inspections, perhaps weekly or even, in extreme cases, daily, or before use. An example of a pre-use check would be the operation of mobile plant. The inspection programme should satisfy any specific legal requirements and reflect risk priorities. Suitable schedules and performance standards for the frequency and content of inspections can help. The schedules can be supplemented with inspection forms or checklists, both to ensure consistency in approach and to provide records for follow-up action.

Inspections should be carried out by people who have the necessary skills and training to identify the relevant hazards and risks and who can assess the conditions found. A properly thought-out approach to inspection will include:

- Well-designed inspection forms to help plan and initiate remedial action by requiring those doing the inspection to rank any deficiencies in order of importance

- Summary lists of remedial action with names and deadlines to track progress on implementing improvements

- Periodic analysis of inspection forms to identify common features or trends that might reveal underlying weakness in the system

- Information to aid judgements about any changes required in the frequency or nature of the inspection programme.

Accident, Ill Health and Incident Investigations

Organisations should have effective procedures in place for reporting and investigating accidents, ill health cases, near misses, and any other incidents. The prime purpose of the investigation procedure is to prevent further accidents or ill health. The occurrence of accidents and ill health is usually evidence of safety and health management failures. In order to find out why an accident, case of ill health or near miss happened, shortcomings in the safety and health management system should be investigated. The investigation procedure should include:

- The types of event to be investigated (e.g. only investigate near misses that could have led to serious harm)

- Co-ordination with emergency plans and procedures where appropriate

- The purpose of investigations

- The scale of investigative effort in relation to the potential or actual harm

- Who is to investigate the accident or ill health case
- The authority of the investigators, their required competencies and associated training needs (including line management)
- Arrangements and location for witness interviews
- Practical issues such as availability of cameras and storage of evidence
- The role of the safety representative in the investigation
- Investigation reporting arrangements, including statutory reporting requirements.

Investigation personnel should begin their preliminary analysis of the facts while further information is collected. Data collection and analysis should continue until an adequate and sufficiently comprehensive explanation is obtained.

Key Data to be Covered in Accident, Ill Health and Incident Reports

The Event

Details of any injured person, including age, sex, experience, training, etc.

- A description of the circumstances, including the place, time of day and conditions
- Details about the event, including:
  - any actions which led directly to the event
  - the direct causes of any injuries, ill health or other loss
  - the immediate causes of the event

— the underlying causes, for example failures in workplace precautions, risk control systems, or management arrangements.

- Details of the outcomes, including in particular:

  — the nature of the outcome, for example injuries or ill health to employees or members of the public, damage to property, process disruptions, emissions to the environment, creation of hazards

  — the severity of the harm caused, including injuries, ill health and losses

  — the immediate management response to the situation and its adequacy

  — was it dealt with promptly?

  — were continuing risks dealt with promptly and adequately?

  — was the first aid response adequate?

  — were emergency procedures followed?

- Whether the event was preventable and, if so, how.

The Potential Consequences

- What was the worst that could have happened?
- What prevented the worst from happening?
- How often could such an event occur (the 'recurrence potential')?
- What was the worst injury or damage which could have resulted (the 'severity potential')?

- How many people could the event have affected (the 'population potential')?

Recommendations

- Prioritised actions with responsibilities and targets for completion

- Whether the risk assessments need to be reviewed and the safety statement updated.

Learning from and Communicating Results from Investigations

The organisation, having learnt from its investigations, should:

- Identify root causes in the safety and health and general management of the organisation

- Communicate findings and recommendations to all relevant parties

- Include relevant findings and recommendations from investigations in the continuing safety and health review process.

The implementation of remedial controls should be monitored to ensure timely and effective change.

Cautions on using Accident and Ill Health Data

Accident and ill health data are important, as they are a direct indicator of safety and health performance. However, some cautions relating to their use are listed below:

- Most organisations have too few injury accidents or cases of work-related ill health to distinguish real trends from random effects.

- If more work is done by the same number of people in the same time, increased workload alone may account for an increase in accident rates.

- The length of absence from work attributed to injury or work-related ill health may be influenced by factors other than the severity of injury or occupational ill health. Such factors can include poor morale, monotonous work, stressful working conditions, poor management–employee relations and local advice or traditions.

- Accidents are often under-reported and occasionally over-reported. Levels of reporting can change. They can improve as a result of increased workforce awareness and better reporting and recording systems.

- A time delay can occur between safety and health management system failures and harmful effects. Moreover, many occupational diseases have long latent periods. Management should not wait for harm to occur before judging whether safety and health management systems are working.

Appendix B

Auditing Systems

Safety and Health Management System Auditing

Auditing is an essential element of a safety and health management system. Safety and health management system auditing is a process that allows the organisation to review and continuously evaluate its safety and health effectiveness. The organisation should evaluate its safety and health performance in order to:

- Maximise knowledge about its effectiveness

- Ensure that appropriate action is taken to improve the control of specific risks

- Improve overall safety and health performance

- Further develop safety and health policies and procedures.

In general, safety and health audits need to consider overall safety and health policy, procedures and the conditions or practices in the workplace. Senior managers should evaluate the overall strategy of the safety and health management system to determine whether it meets the needs of the organisation, its shareholders and the regulatory authorities. This will allow them to provide directional feedback to the organisation, and help them determine future priorities for meaningful planning and continual improvement.

Board and Senior Management Commitment to Auditing

For safety and health auditing to be of value, the board of directors of the organisation and its senior management should be fully committed to the concept of auditing and its effective implementation in the organisation. This includes a commitment to consider audit findings and recommendations and to take appropriate action as necessary, within an appropriate time. Senior and line management should recognise that, once they have agreed that an audit should be carried out, it should be completed in an impartial way.

Co-operation with the Auditors

All relevant personnel should be informed of the purposes and benefits of auditing. Staff should be encouraged to co-operate fully with the auditors and to respond to their questions honestly.

Essential Elements of a Safety and Health Management System Audit

Safety and health auditing should include the following essential elements.

Formal Auditing

Formal auditing provides a comprehensive and formal assessment of the organisation's compliance with safety and health procedures and practices. The end result of a formal audit should include a detailed written assessment of safety and health procedures, the level of compliance with procedures and practices and, where necessary, should identify corrective actions.

Regular and Ad Hoc Inspections

Regular and ad hoc inspections provide a means of checking compliance with individual safety and health requirements.

The results of these audits and inspections should be fed back to the relevant parties as soon as possible to allow corrective action to be taken. As many employees as practicable, including the safety representative, should be involved when auditing activities in their work areas.

Planning and Managing Safety and Health Management System Audits

Audit Programme

A programme of auditing should be prepared and included in the safety statement. Factors that may need to be taken into account when deciding the frequency of audits include: the nature of the hazards; an adverse audit or incident record; and any legislative requirements.

Auditor Selection, Competence and Training

One or more people can undertake audits. A team approach may widen involvement and improve co-operation. External or internal auditors may be used, but preference should be given to internal auditors if the expertise is available. In either case, they should be independent of the part of the organisation or the activity that is to be audited.

Auditors need to understand their task and be competent to carry it out. They need to have the experience and knowledge of the relevant safety and health standards and the systems they are auditing to enable them to evaluate performance and identify deficiencies. Auditors should be familiar with the requirements set out in any relevant safety and health legislation so that they can identify unsafe behaviour that would not be reflected in the organisation's documents and records. In addition, auditors should be aware of and have access to standards and authoritative guidance relevant to the work they are engaged in.

Data Collection and Interpretation

The techniques and aids used to collect information will depend on the nature of the audit being undertaken. A representative sample of key activities should be included in the audit and key personnel should be interviewed. Relevant documentation should be examined. This may include:

- Safety and health management system documentation
- Risk assessments and the safety statement
- Safety and health and emergency procedures
- Permit-to-work systems and confined space entry procedures
- Minutes of safety and health meetings
- Accident/incident reports and records
- Any reports or communication from the HSA (e.g. oral reports and advice, letters, notices)
- Statutory registers and certificates
- Training records.

The value of an audit depends on the experience and knowledge of the auditors and their ability to interpret observations and elaborate on their findings. It is also dependent on the integrity of all parties involved. Wherever possible, checks should be built into the system to help to avoid misinterpretation or misapplication of audit records.

Audit Reporting

At the end of the audit, the auditor or audit team should summarise and feed back their initial findings to the manager responsible and, in particular, draw attention to any issues that are so significant that they need immediate action. The audit report should assess overall performance, identify any inadequacies and make recommendations on action for improvement.

Acting on Audit Results

An action plan of agreed remedial measures should be drawn up together with identification of responsible persons, completion dates and reporting requirements. Follow-up monitoring arrangements have to be established to ensure satisfactory implementation of the recommendations.

Effective Safety and Health Audit Systems

Effective auditing systems are carried out by a competent individual or team specifically trained to do the work (this may involve a team of managers, specialists, other employees or their representatives, or external consultants). The auditor(s) is/are independent of the area or section being audited.

Audits are designed to assess the key elements of safety and health management listed below.

Safety and Health Policy

Intent, scope and adequacy of the safety and health policy.

Organisation:

- Acceptance of safety and health responsibilities by line managers and the adequacy of arrangements to secure control

- Existence and thoroughness of safety and health documentation

- Adequacy of arrangements to consult and involve all employees in safety and health

- Adequacy of arrangements to communicate policy and relevant information

- Adequacy of arrangements to ensure the competence of all employees and the provision of safety and health assistance

- Level of emergency prevention, preparedness and response

- Contacting and procurement procedures

- Worker participation and effectiveness in promoting full worker participation.

Planning and implementation:

- Overall control and direction of the safety and health effort

- Adequacy of management arrangements, risk control systems and workplace precautions

- Extent of compliance with relevant safety and health laws

- Adequacy of resources and their proportional allocation to reflect the hazard profile of the business

- Extent of compliance with management arrangements and performance standards, and the effectiveness of workplace precautions in controlling risk

- Long-term improvement in accident and incident performance

- Effectiveness of promoting full worker participation.

Measuring systems:

- Adequacy, relevance and design of measuring systems

Reviewing systems:

- Ability of the organisation to learn from experience, improve performance, develop the safety and health management system and respond to change.

References

International

Guidelines on Occupational Safety and Health Management Systems, International Labour Office, Geneva, ILO – OSH 2001.

Successful Health and Safety Management (2nd edition), HSG 65, HSE Books, London 1997.

Strategies to Promote Safe Behaviour as Part of a Health and Safety Management System, HSE, UK Contract Research Report 430/2002.

Guide to Occupational Health and Safety Management Systems, BS 8800, British Standards Institution, London 2004.

Occupational Health and Safety Management Systems – Specification, OHSAS 18001:1999 and *Guidelines for the Implementation of OHSAS 18001*, OHSAS 18002:2000, National Standards Authority Ireland (NSAI).

Systems in Focus: Guidance on Occupational Safety and Health Management Systems, Institution of Occupational Safety and Health, UK 2003.

HSA Guidance

The HSA has produced many publications that can be consulted for further information when preparing and implementing a safety statement or developing a safety and health management system. They cover:

- Specific workplace hazards, e.g. on manual handling, noise, stress, violence, bullying, chemicals, carcinogens, asbestos, petroleum and confined spaces
- Certain work sectors, e.g. for construction, quarries, agriculture, forestry, chemical processing, LPG filling, offices, shops, transport of dangerous goods, security industry, hotels, catering and restaurants, retail and distribution
- Sector specific safety statements, e.g. for agriculture, shops, fishing vessels, small businesses
- Other work-related issues, e.g. on safety representatives and consultation, obligatory safety signs, pregnancy and work child safety on farms, safety and workplace vehicles, rider

operated lift trucks, occupational asthma, safety consultation and representation, scaffolding, cranes and roof work.

All of these publications are available from the HSA website at www.hsa.ie/eng/Publications_and_Forms/Publications/. Most are free of charge. Priced publications are also available from HSA Publications at 1890 289 389.

Appendix C

Safety Culture (Common Topic 4)

Introduction

Note: Safety culture is an important topic, but time-consuming to inspect (because of the sample required) and difficult to tackle. It is recommended that it is only taken on where there is good reason to believe that there is a significant issue to address, such as a poor safety record over a period, and where the company is likely to be receptive to advice.

An organisation's culture can have as big an influence on safety outcomes as the safety management system. 'Safety culture' is a subset of the overall company culture.

What is safety culture?

'The safety culture of an organisation is the product of individual and group values, attitudes, perceptions, competencies, and patterns of behaviour that determine the commitment to, and the style and proficiency of, an organisation's health and safety management. Organisations with a positive safety culture are characterised by communications founded on mutual trust, by shared perceptions of the importance of safety and by confidence in the efficiency of preventive measures.'

ACSNI Human Factors Study Group: Third Report, *Organising for Safety*, HSE Books 1993.

Many companies talk about 'safety culture' when referring to the inclination of their employees to comply with rules or act safety or unsafely. However, we find that the culture and style of management is even more significant, for example a natural, unconscious bias for production over safety, or a tendency to focus on the short term and to be highly reactive.

Symptoms of poor culture factors can include:

- Widespread, routine procedural violations

- Failure to comply with the company's own safety management system (although either of these can also be due to poor procedure design)

- Management decisions that appear consistently to put production or cost before safety.

In inspection, it is possible to gather evidence about a company's culture, although this requires interviewing a suitably representative sample of people from all levels of the organisation.

Key Aspects of an Effective Safety Culture

Management Commitment

Management commitment produces higher levels of motivation and concern for health and safety throughout the organisation. It is indicated by the proportion of resources (time, money, people) and support allocated to health and safety management and by the status given to health and safety versus production, costs, etc. The active involvement of senior management in the health and safety system is very important.

Visible Management

Managers need to be seen to lead by example when it comes to health and safety. Good managers appear regularly on the 'shop floor', talk about health and safety and visibly demonstrate their commitment by their actions – such as stopping production to resolve issues. It is important that management is perceived as sincerely committed to safety. If not, employees will generally assume that they are expected to put commercial interests first, and safety initiatives or programmes will be undermined by cynicism.

Good Communication at All Levels

In a positive culture questions about health and safety should be part of everyday work conversations. Management should listen actively to what they are being told by employees, and take what they hear seriously.

Active employee participation in safety is important, to build ownership of safety at all levels and exploit the unique knowledge that employees have of their own work. This can include active involvement in workshops, risk assessments, plant design, etc. In companies with a good culture, you will find that the story from employees and management is consistent, and safety is seen as a joint exercise.

Inspection

Inspection needs to involve interviewing a suitable cross-section of the company, particularly a reasonable number of employees, who should be interviewed in a non-threatening manner. The number needs to be sufficient to take account of differing views and experience. Given this condition the open questions given in the question set will provide a helpful picture of the overall style of the company.

Note: unless the inspector has significant personal experience of trying to tackle safety culture, it would be best to simply reflect back what has been found, and give general rather than specific advice on how to improve it.

Specific Documents

In addition to the general documents that should be requested prior to the visit, the following documents, which are specific to this topic, should also be requested:

- results of climate/attitude/opinion surveys
- results of procedure surveys.

Enforcement and Advice

Clearly, safety culture itself is not enforceable, and interventions are generally reserved for receptive companies, or as part of an overall incident investigation. However, there can be enforcement to address the outcomes of a poor culture. For example, if a company is unsuccessfully relying on procedural controls to avoid major accidents, there could be enforcement of management arrangements, through the hierarchy of control, to either ensure compliance or provide alternative safeguards.

In one example, an improvement notice was issued to a company on implementing a safety management system, including identification and control of human reliability risks, and the company subsequently managed to reduce accidents by over 50%. The 2003 investigation report for BP Grangemouth was partly the result of an investigation into culture factors underlying a series of major incidents. There have since been several other field interventions, generally seen as valuable by the company and site inspector.

Guidance

- *Successful Health and Safety Management*, HSG 65

- *Reducing Error and Influencing Behaviour*, HSG 48

- ACSNI Study Group on Human Factors, Third Report: *Organising for Safety: Advisory Committee on the Safety of Nuclear Installations* (1993, reprinted 1998)

- *Health and Safety Climate Survey Tool*, HSE Books, ISBN 071761462X.

Appendix D

Sample Forms and Additional Information

Nifast Risk Assessment Tool

Two factors are considered when determining risk:

1. **Likelihood:** the likelihood of an accident occurring

2. **Severity:** the severity of the potential outcome of that accident.

Both are rated on a scale of 1 to 3:

Likelihood		Severity	
1	Unlikely	1	Slightly harmful
2	Likely	2	Harmful
3	Very likely	3	Very harmful

Guidelines for determining severity:

Slightly Harmful	Harmful	Very Harmful
• superficial injuries • minor cuts and bruises • eye irritation from dust • nuisance and irritation • temporary discomfort	• lacerations • burns • concussion • serious sprains • minor fractures • dermatitis • asthma • minor disability	• amputation • major fractures • poisoning • fatal injuries • occupational cancer • deafness • fatal disease • head injuries • eye injuries

The risk is calculated by multiplying the two factors:

Risk = Likelihood x Severity

For example:

Likelihood	=	Unlikely	=	**1**
Severity	=	Very harmful	=	**3**
Risk rating (RR)	=	**1 x 3**	=	**3**

		Severity		
		Slightly harmful	Harmful	Very harmful
Likelihood	Unlikely	1	2	3
	Likely	2	4	6
	Very likely	3	6	9

Assessment	Priority	Action
Trivial Risk **RR = 1**	Non-urgent	No action needed
Acceptable Risk **RR = 2**	Non-urgent	No additional controls Monitoring required Assessment recorded
Moderate Risk **RR = 3 or 4**	Action needed	Controls required as soon as practical Assessment recorded Controls documented
Substantial Risk **RR = 6**	Urgent action needed	Controls required immediately Assessment recorded Controls documented
Intolerable Risk **RR = 9**	Urgent action needed	Work prohibited/ceased Controls required immediately Assessment recorded Controls documented Work stoppage documented

Sample Risk Assessment Form

Area/Dept/Activity:			Date of Assessment:			
			Assessment Undertaken By:			
			Assessment Review Date:			

Hazard & Risk	People at Risk	Existing Controls	Current Risk		
			L	S	RR
Hazard:					
Illness/Injury:		• Person Responsible:			

Action Plan

Hazard	People at Risk	Date Action to be Completed	Revised Risk		
			L	S	RR
	• Person Responsible:				

Sample Accident/Incident Report Form

☐ INJURY ☐ NON-INJURY (Incident)	Form Number:

Section 1 – *Facts and circumstances related to the Accident/Incident*			
Employee Name (Print)	Name of Manager / Supervisor	☐ In Company ☐ Contractor	Department
Date of Accident / Incident	Time of Accident/ Incident (24 hrs)	Accident/Incident Reported Date: _____ Time: _____	To whom was accident/incident first reported?
Nature of injury & body part injured e.g. right thumb, left eye	Exact activity being done:	Exact location of accident /incident:	Protective Equipment Worn ☐ Yes ☐ No ☐ N/A If yes, give details:
	Occurred during Instruction ☐ Yes ☐ No	**For Manager Use only:**	☐ Reportable to Insurance Company ☐ Reported to Contractor ☐ Reportable to HAS

The Outcome

First Aid Treatment Given:	Detail first aid supplies used:
_____	_____
_____	_____
_____	_____
_____	**Location of supplies used:**
_____	_____
_____	_____
_____	_____

Outcome: ☐ Sent to Hospital ☐ Back to work ☐ Went home ☐ Sent to Company Doctor ☐ Sent to Nifast Company Doctor ☐ N/A ☐ Other, specify	First Aider's Name: _____
Date and Time Lost Work Days Began: _____	Date of Return to Work: _____

The Property Damage (in the Event of Property Damage)

Nature of Damage:	Estimated Repair Cost:	Estimated Down Time:
Date damage was reported/discovered:	Actual Cost:	Actual Down Time:

Description of Accident/Incident

Describe so that a person unfamiliar with your plant and operation will understand. Give necessary background, the victim's position relative to his/her surroundings, what he/she was doing, what triggered the accident, the source of injury, the accident type, etc.

_____

_____

_____

_____

_____

_____

_____

_____

_____

_____

_____

Name of Witnesses: (Print)	Injured Person/Witness Account Record
_____ _____ ☐ N/A	☐ Attached ☐ Not Required ☐ To Follow

Section 2 – *Causes of the accident/incident*

* Check at least one item (i.e. as many as apply) in <u>each quadrant</u>. If none/others apply then check that item.

IMMEDIATE CAUSES (check at least one item)*

UNSAFE CONDITIONS

1. ☐ Lack of or inadequate guards or safety devices
2. ☐ Lack of or inadequate warning system
3. ☐ Poor housekeeping hazards
4. ☐ Hazardous arrangement, placement or storage
5. ☐ Close clearance and congestion hazards
6. ☐ Unexpected movement hazards
7. ☐ Hazardous defect of tools, equipment, materials, etc.
8. ☐ Inadequate/unavailable protective equipment
9. ☐ Inadequate/excessive lighting
10. ☐ Inadequate ventilation
11. ☐ Fire/explosion hazard
12. ☐ Excessive noise
13. ☐ Over-exposure to hazardous agents
14. ☐ High/low temperature exposure
15. ☐ Adverse weather conditions
16. ☐ Mechanical/material failure
17. ☐ Structural defects
18. ☐ Inadequate security
19. ☐ Inadequate lock out/tag out
20. ☐ Other than above (Specify)

_____

☐ None

IMMEDIATE CAUSES (check at least one item)*

UNSAFE ACTIONS

1. ☐ Operating or using equipment without authority
2. ☐ Deviation from policy, procedure, guideline
3. ☐ Failure to secure or make safe equipment
4. ☐ Operating or working at an unsafe speed
5. ☐ Making safety devices inoperative
6. ☐ Using defective tools or equipment
7. ☐ Using improper tools or equipment
8. ☐ Using tools or equipment unsafely
9. ☐ Taking an unsafe position or posture
10. ☐ Servicing moving, energised equipment
11. ☐ Riding hazardous moving equipment
12. ☐ Horseplay, distracting, startling, teasing, etc.
13. ☐ Improper lifting techniques
14. ☐ Improper loading or placement
15. ☐ Failure to use or misuse of protective equipment
16. ☐ Attempted to clear blockage with hand
17. ☐ Other than above (Specify)

_____

☐ None

PERSONAL FACTORS (check at least one item)*	**JOB FACTORS** (check at least one item)*
1. ☐ Failure to abide by policy, procedure, guidelines	1. ☐ Training not complete
2. ☐ Hazardous personal attire	2. ☐ Inadequate policies, procedures, guidelines
3. ☐ Acted to avoid discomfort	3. ☐ Failure to implement a preventive maintenance programme
4. ☐ Influence of pre-existing condition	4. ☐ Failure to carry out repairs
5. ☐ Stress	5. ☐ Equipment/tools used by untrained/unauthorised personnel
6. ☐ Fatigue	6. ☐ Inadequate engineering or safety reviews
7. ☐ Tried to gain or save time	7. ☐ Inadequate tools/equipment
8. ☐ Poor motivation/monotonous task	8. ☐ Unavailability of tools and equipment
9. ☐ Other than above (Specify)	9. ☐ Incorrect tools or equipment specified
_____	10. ☐ Failure to establish safe purchasing standards
☐ None	11. ☐ Failure to establish contractor safety standards and controls
	12. ☐ Design layout inadequate
	13. ☐ Ergonomic consideration – inadequate/improper
	14. ☐ Improper storage of material
	15. ☐ Other than above (Specify)
	_____
	☐ None

Section 3 – *Controls to prevent recurrence*

Corrective Action Required

Check those actions taken to prevent recurrence. Fill in the appropriate box for corrective actions decided upon or planned but not yet initiated or completed.

☐ Re-training of those involved	☐ Re-training of others doing the job	☐ Re-training of others
☐ Temporary reassignment of person	☐ Permanent reassignment of person	☐ Action to improve inspection
☐ Action to improve housekeeping	☐ Order job hazard analysis	☐ Equipment repair or replacement
☐ Action to improve design/layout	☐ Action to improve construction	☐ Installation of guard or safety device
☐ Correction of unnecessary congestion	☐ Improved PPE	☐ Order regular pre-job instruction
☐ Order use of safer materials	☐ Check with manufacturer	☐ Inform all instructors/ consultants
☐ Initiate further investigation	☐ Revise instructions	☐ Undertake ergonomic assessment
☐ Reprimand of those involved	☐ Other than above	

Describe details of your corrective action: _____

_____

_____

_____

_____

Person Responsible for Corrective Action: _____

Target Date: _____

Section 4 – *Sign off*		
Injured Person	Signature	Date
Manager	Signature	Date
First Aider	Signature	Date
Witness	Signature	Date
Designated Safety Officer	Signature	Date

Fire Safety Programme

SAFETY AUDITING PROCEDURES (sample)			
HAZARD AUDIT CHECKLIST			
AREA:_____ AUDITOR:_____ DATE:_____			

Hazard No. 1 – Fire

QUESTIONS	ANSWERS		
Are all extinguishers wall mounted?	☐ Yes	☐ No	☐ N/A
Is all firefighting equipment accessible?	☐ Yes	☐ No	☐ N/A
Is all firefighting equipment serviced?	☐ Yes	☐ No	☐ N/A
Are portable extinguishers applicable to materials used?	☐ Yes	☐ No	☐ N/A
Is firefighting equipment visibly marked?	☐ Yes	☐ No	☐ N/A

Are 'No smoking' signs posted?	☐ Yes	☐ No	☐ N/A
Are 'No smoking' signs observed?	☐ Yes	☐ No	☐ N/A
Are all escape routes unobstructed?	☐ Yes	☐ No	☐ N/A
Are all escape routes signposted from the workplace?	☐ Yes	☐ No	☐ N/A
Can emergency exits be easily opened?	☐ Yes	☐ No	☐ N/A
Are staff trained in the use of firefighting equipment?	☐ Yes	☐ No	☐ N/A
Are fire doors in area kept closed?	☐ Yes	☐ No	☐ N/A
Have sprinkler heads a minimum clearance from material storage and furnishings (455mm)?	☐ Yes	☐ No	☐ N/A
Are flammable liquids contained in approved safety cans and labelled?	☐ Yes	☐ No	☐ N/A
Are flammable liquids in the workplace kept to a minimum?	☐ Yes	☐ No	☐ N/A
Has the fire alarm been checked and are records available?	☐ Yes	☐ No	☐ N/A
Are all exit signs illuminated?	☐ Yes	☐ No	☐ N/A

Inspection	Frequency	Person Responsible
General Inspection	Daily	Fire Warden
Fire Alarm	Daily/Weekly	Fire Safety Officer or Fire Warden
	Quarterly/Yearly	Qualified Person
Emergency Lighting	Weekly	Fire Safety Officer or Fire Warden
	Quarterly/Yearly	Qualified Person
Firefighting Equipment	Daily/Monthly	Fire Safety Officer or Fire Warden
	Yearly	Qualified Person
Electrical (non-technical)	Monthly	Fire Safety Officer
Kitchen	Monthly	Fire Safety Officer
Emergency Exits/Routes	Weekly/Monthly	Fire Safety Officer or Fire Warden
Fire Doors	Monthly	Fire Safety Officer
Upholstery	Monthly	Fire Safety Officer
Extraction System	Monthly	Fire Safety Officer
Isolation Valves	Monthly	Fire Safety Officer
Compartment Integrity	Monthly	Fire Safety Officer

Details

General Inspection

This should be carried out daily by the fire warden in each area. It should include evacuation routes, final exits, fire points, fire alarm panels and general housekeeping.

Fire Alarm (Ref. I.S. 3218)

The daily check involves ensuring that the panel is in the 'green' operative mode.

The weekly test entails operating a break glass unit to check that the entire alarm system is functioning. It also involves checking the batteries. The results are entered into the fire register.

As with all fire systems and equipment, where a quarterly, six-monthly or annual test is called for, it must be carried out by a qualified person, i.e. the supplier or other qualified contractor.

Emergency Lighting (Ref. I.S. 3217)

The weekly test involves a visual examination of the luminaires, LEDs and panel(s). Where appropriate a battery check should be included.

Quarterly, a power failure should be simulated for a minimum of 30 minutes.

Annually, each installation should be tested to ensure conformity with the code. Each luminaire should be tested for full duration.

Firefighting Equipment (Ref. I.S. 291)

All firefighting equipment should be visually checked every day to ensure that it is both in place and available for use.

The monthly test will include a physical examination of equipment, to include seals, etc., and also the fire points for damage or obstruction.

The annual test will be carried out by a qualified contractor or specialist.

Electrical (Non-Technical)

The monthly inspection involves checking:

- damaged/defensive plugs, sockets, switches, thermostats, etc.
- damaged/loose cables, wires, connections (particularly to portable equipment), etc.

Such faults are to be notified and remedial work should be carried out immediately

Kitchen

The monthly inspection involves ensuring that:

- filters, extractor hoods and cooking surfaces are free from grease accumulations
- all thermostats are functioning correctly
- cooking oil in deep fat fryers, etc. is changed regularly.

These checks should be carried out by the fire safety officer and the head chef.

Emergency Exits

- Daily inspection: ensure that all escape routes are freely accessible, unobstructed and unlocked.

- Monthly inspection: check for mechanical defects, door fit and to ensure that the 'Push Bar to Open' sign is intact and legible.

Fire Doors

- Monthly inspection: ensure that the self-closing device is functioning, that the door closes fully and correctly, that the intumescent seals are in place and undamaged, and that the 'Fire Door – Keep Closed' sign is intact and legible.

Upholstery

Monthly inspection: check that all upholstery fabric is in good condition, i.e. that there are no tears or excessive wear.

Extraction System

Monthly inspection: ensure that the manufacturer's recommendations on inspection, servicing and maintenance of the system are adhered to.

Isolation Valves

Monthly inspection: check that all isolation valves (i.e. gas, oil, electricity) operate freely, are free from obstruction and are known to relevant staff members.

Compartment Integrity

Monthly inspection: ensure that any maintenance work involving penetration of walls, floors or ceilings for the carriage of pipes, cable runs or other such work will be properly fire stopped and closed off.

Conclusion

This fire safety programme will include weekly reports on the current status of individual areas. It will also include maintaining the fire register for, and liaison with, the local fire authority.

More detailed inspections should be undertaken as per the following schedule.

Electrical Inspection and Testing Schedule for Offices

Recommended electrical inspection and testing schedule[1] for offices			
Equipment/ Environment	**User Checks**	**Formal Visual Inspection**	**Combined Inspection and Testing**
Battery operated (less than 20 volts)	No[2]	No	No
Extra low voltage (less than 50 volts AC), e.g. telephone equipment, low-voltage desk lights	No[2]	No	No

IT, e.g. desktop computers, VDU screens	No[2]	Yes Every 2–4 years	No if double insulated – otherwise up to 5 years
Photocopiers, fax machines – **not** hand held, rarely moved	No[2]	Yes Every 2–4 years	No if double insulated – otherwise up to 5 years
Not hand held, moved occasionally, e.g. fans, table lamps, slide projectors	No[2]	Yes Every 2–4 years	No
Double insulated equipment, **hand held**, e.g. some floor cleaners	Yes	Yes Every 6 months–1 year	No
Earthed equipment (Class 1), e.g. electric kettles, toasters, some floor cleaners	Yes	Yes Every 6 months–1 year	Yes Every 1–2 years
Cables (leads) and plugs connected to the above	Yes	Yes Every 6 months–4 years depending on the type of equipment it is connected to	Yes Every 1–5 years depending on the type of equipment it is connected to

Notes

Inspection and testing requires a higher degree of competence than visual inspections, but may be carried out after limited training using one of the test kits now available commercially. Equipment is plugged into the kit and an array of indicators identifies whether the equipment is properly earthed, etc. This work can be contracted to a qualified electrician. Equipment which fails on test should be taken out of service and subject to repair or maintenance.

[1] Experience of operating the inspection and testing schedule outlined in the table over a period of time, together with information on faults found, should be used to review the frequency of inspection. It should also be used to review whether and how often equipment and associated leads and plugs should receive a combined inspection and test. This may be reviewed and decided upon either by a manager, with guidance from the relevant competent person, or by the team carrying out the electrical inspections.

[2] 'No' means no formal, recorded checks, but users should always visually inspect equipment to be used, and respond to any evidence of fault or damage.

Hazardous Chemicals (CLP/CPL Regulations)

Sources of Safety Information

The hazards presented by chemical agents must be clearly identified and information on the hazards and controls must be available for all persons who handle, manufacture or store chemical agents.

There are two sets of regulations defining the safety information that must be provided for chemical products:

- The 'new' **CLP Regulations** (Classification, Labelling and Packaging) implement the United Nation's Globally Harmonised System (GHS).

- The 'old' **CPL Regulations** (Classification, Packaging and Labelling) implement a number of EC Directives (only apply in Europe).

CLP Regulations

Labelling

A dangerous substance to which the CLP Regulations apply must be labelled. The labelling system is distinct from the UN transport warning labels, and must include the following information:

- Name of the substance
- Name and full address of the person responsible for placing the substance on the market
- A list of hazardous ingredients
- Hazard pictograms
- Hazard statements and precautionary statements.

Hazard Pictograms

These are black graphics shown in a red-edged diamond. The common hazard classes are given here:

Pictogram	Class	What It Means
	Explosive	May explode if subject to heat, shock or friction

	Oxidiser	Produces heat on reaction with other materials and creates a fire risk when in contact with flammable or combustible materials
	Gas Under Pressure	May explode if heated
	Flammable (gases, aerosols, liquids or solids)	Combustible chemicals. They will burn readily, if oxygen and a source of ignition are present They may form explosive mixtures with air
	Corrosive	Can cause chemical burns to skin and eyes (may also be corrosive to certain metals) PPE to protect the skin and eyes is essential

	Irritant	Can cause irritation to skin, eyes or, if inhaled, to breathing
	Skin Sensitiser	A substance that can lead to hypersensitivity or an allergic response of the skin
	Harmful	May cause limited health risks if inhaled, swallowed or penetrates the skin
	Acute Toxicity	May cause serious health risks or death if swallowed, inhaled or if it penetrates the skin

Access must be restricted to trained and experienced staff |

	Carcinogen	Substances which induce cancer or increase its incidence
	Mutagen	Substances giving rise to an increased occurrence of mutations in populations of cells
	Reproductive Toxin	Substances which cause adverse effects on sexual function and fertility as well as developmental toxicity in the offspring
	Respiratory Sensitisers	A substance that can lead to hypersensitivity or an allergic response of the respiratory system
	Specific Target Organ Toxins	Substances that cause damage to specific organs in the body
	Hazardous to the Aquatic Environment	Substances which can cause damage to the aquatic environment

Signal Words

The words **Danger** or **Warning** may accompany the pictogram to indicate the severity of the hazard. **Danger** is the most severe, **Warning** is less severe.

Hazard Statements and Precautionary Statements

These are from a standard list. The hazard statements describe the hazard associated with the chemical. The precautionary statements describe the safety precautions to take when handling a chemical.

Examples of **hazard statements**:

- H226: flammable liquid and vapour
- H318: causes serious eye damage
- H400: very toxic to aquatic life.

Note:

- H200s indicate physical hazards
- H300s indicate toxicological hazards
- H400s indicate environmental hazards
- EUHs give Supplemental Hazard Information (EU only)

Examples of **precautionary statements**:

- P102: Keep out of reach of children
- P270: Do not eat, drink or smoke when using this product
- P302 + P352: If on skin: Wash with plenty of soap and water
- P402: Store in a dry place.

Note:

- P100s relate to general precautions

- P200s relate to prevention

- P300s relate to response

- P400s relate to storage

- P500s relate to disposal

Safety Data Sheets

Manufacturers are required to supply users with a safety data sheet (SDS) containing specific technical information on the risks connected with the chemical as well as safety data detailing the protective measures advised.

The SDS must contain information under the following 16 headings

1. Identification of the substance/preparation and of the company/undertaking

2. Hazards identification

3. Composition/information on ingredients

4. First aid measures

5. Firefighting measures

6. Accidental release measures

7. Handling and storage

8. Exposure controls/personal protection

9. Physical and chemical properties

10. Stability and reactivity

11. Toxicological information

12. Ecological information

13. Disposal considerations

14. Transport information

15. Regulatory information

16. Other information

Implementation

Transition periods:

- Pure substances had until 1 December 2010
- Mixtures have until 1 June 2015
- Products already placed on the market (on the shelf or in the warehouse) after these dates, will be/were given a two-year extension so that they will not have to be repackaged or relabelled.

Until 1 June 2015, the label of mixtures can follow the format of the old CPL system (orange symbols) or the new CLP scheme (diamond pictograms). After that date, or two years later if already placed on the market, it must follow the new CLP Regulations.

CPL Regulations

The European system for labelling chemicals will still be visible in the years to come. The main differences are highlighted below:

Hazard symbols are equivalent to the pictograms in the CLP Regulations.

Explosive

Oxidiser

Highly Flammable and Extremely Flammable

Corrosive

Toxic and Very Toxic

Harmful and Irritant

Dangerous to the Environment

Risk phrases describe the hazards associated with the chemical (similar to the hazard statements in the CLP Regulations, e.g. R10 – Flammable; R20 – Harmful for Inhalation.

Safety phrases describe the safety precautions to take when handling a chemical (similar to the precautionary statements in the CLP Regulations), e.g. S16 – Keep away from sources of ignition – no smoking; S46 – If swallowed seek medical advice immediately and show this label or container.

Control Measures

Employers are required to prevent or adequately control exposure to chemical agents. There is a hierarchy of control measures for chemicals in the workplace, outlined below.

Elimination

Eliminating the chemical, or the process that requires the chemical, is the ideal option.

- Eliminate the use of paints and varnish by leaving wooden furniture untreated

- The smoking ban eliminated tobacco smoke from indoor workplaces

Substitution

Substitute the hazardous chemical agent for a safe or less hazardous alternative:

- Lead-free paints used in place of lead-based paints

- Asbestos replaced by synthetic mineral fibres

- Rosin-based solder flux replaced by rosin-free alternative.

Alternatively, substitute one form of the hazardous chemical for another form of the same chemical:

- Powdered ingredients replaced with pellets, which release less dust

- Paint instead of spraying when applying surface coatings.

Engineering Controls

These include:

- Automated production lines, which can use robots for spraying components or wave soldering units for assembly of electronics

- Vacuum transfer systems for powders

- Extraction systems, including fume cupboards or local exhaust ventilation.

Administrative Controls

These include:

- Reduced periods of exposure
- Job rotation
- Restricted non-essential access
- Standard operating procedures
- Good housekeeping.

Personal Protective Equipment

Personal protective equipment (PPE) and respiratory protective equipment (RPE) should only be used where exposure cannot be prevented by other means. PPE and RPE includes:

- gloves
- masks
- safety glasses, goggles and visors
- overalls, lab coats or aprons
- boots.

Bullying and Harassment in the Workplace

Definition

The Government Task Force on Bullying defines workplace bullying as follows:

> *Workplace bullying is repeated inappropriate behaviour, direct or indirect, whether verbal, physical or otherwise, conducted by one or more persons against another or others, at the place of work and/or in the course of employment, which could reasonably be regarded as undermining the individual's right to dignity at work.*

An isolated incident of the behaviour described in this definition may be an affront to dignity at work but a once-off incident is not considered to be bullying.

Bullying manifests itself as various types of behaviour, including behaviour which may:

- humiliate
- intimidate
- verbally abuse
- victimise
- exclude and isolate
- intrude through pestering, spying or stalking
- give repeated unreasonable assignments to duties which are obviously unfavourable to one individual
- give repeated impossible deadlines or impossible tasks
- imply threats.

The above list is representative only, not exhaustive, and it should be used as guidance. These are types of inappropriate behaviour that undermine an individual's right to dignity at work and can constitute bullying.

The Employment Equality Act 1998 protects employees from employment-related harassment and sexual harassment. The definition of sexual harassment includes:

- Any act of physical intimacy

- Request for sexual favours

- Other act or conduct including spoken words, gestures or the production, display or circulation of written words, pictures or other material that is unwelcome and could reasonably be regarded as sexually offensive, humiliating or intimidating.

The definition of harassment in the Employment Equality Act 1998 is similar to that of sexual harassment but without the sexual element. The harassment has to be based on the relevant characteristic of the employee, whether marital status, sexual orientation, religious belief (or none), age, disability, race, colour, nationality or ethnic or national origin, or membership of the Traveller community.

Many forms of behaviour may constitute harassment, including:

- **Verbal** harassment: jokes, comments, ridicule or songs

- **Written** harassment: including faxes, text messages, emails or notices

- **Physical** harassment: jostling, shoving or any form of assault

- **Intimidatory** harassment: gestures, posturing or threatening poses

- **Visual displays** such as posters, emblems or badges

- **Isolation** or exclusion from social activities

- **Pressure** to behave in a manner that the employee thinks is inappropriate, for example being required to dress in a manner unsuited to their ethnic or religious background.

Bullying /Harassment and the Law

Harassment is also a criminal offence under the Non-Fatal Offences against the Person Act 1997 and a number of prosecutions have been brought against employees in Ireland (and in Britain under comparable legislation) where, for example, employees have sent pornographic email messages to work colleagues.

The *Report of the Task Force on the Prevention of Workplace Bullying* pointed out that the general duties of employers in the 1989 Act (now the 2005 Act), and the requirement to have a safety statement based on comprehensive risk assessments, cover the area of bullying and harassment in general terms.

Intention

The intention of the perpetrator of the harassment or sexual harassment is irrelevant. The fact that the perpetrator has no intention of harassing or sexually harassing the employee is no defence. The effect of the behaviour on the employee is what is important.

Codes of Practice

There are three Codes of Practice on Workplace Bullying and Harassment because there are three separate pieces of legislation relating to this aspect of employment:

* Safety, Health and Welfare at Work Act 2005

* Industrial Relations Act 1990

* Employment Equality Act 1998.

The Codes of Practice are designed to provide guidelines on arrangements, procedures and general guidance on tackling workplace bullying, harassment and sexual harassment.

- HSA: *Code of Practice for Employers and Employees on the Prevention and Resolution of Workplace Bullying*

- Department of Enterprise and Employment: *Code of Practice Detailing Procedures for Addressing Bullying in the Workplace*

- Equality Authority: *Code of Practice on Sexual Harassment and Harassment at Work*.

Anti-Bullying and Harassment Policy

Bullying is a bit like a plant in an organisation – it can be nurtured and allowed to flourish or it can be starved and got rid of. The culture in the organisation will be the key determining factor. Organisations should have an anti-bullying/harassment policy which should contain the following elements:

- Stated intolerance of bullying and harassment

- Definition and examples of workplace bullying and harassment

- Senior management commitment

- Rights and responsibilities of all parties

- Procedures (both informal and formal) for addressing allegations

- List of contact officers

- Training and awareness.

Dealing with Problems

The widest range of options should be available to employees who feel they are being bullied or harassed, as follows:

Informal Approach: Self-initiated

These are attempts at resolution taken by the person being bullied.

Confronting:

- Sends a strong message that the person has identified the behaviours
- Prevents or stops the 'put-down slide'
- Empowering
- Rarely affects a bully's attitude, but may affect their behaviour
- May even make the behaviour worse.

When to confront:

- Over less serious incidents of bullying
- If the person is not seriously affected
- When they feel it might achieve something.

The contact officer's role is to:

- Help the individual to determine whether confronting is appropriate
- Explain what it entails and possible implications
- Coach the person.

Informal Approach: Assisted

This should be:

- Made orally

- Made to relevant personnel

- Not officially recorded

- Confidential and non-confrontational

- Dealt with in a low-key manner, without apportioning blame.

Formal Complaints

After a complaint has been made (in writing), the procedure is:

- Inform alleged perpetrator of complaint in writing

- Terms of reference agreed

- Investigator appointed

- Investigation conducted.

Conducting Investigations

The investigator will be guided by:

- Principles of natural justice

- Policy definitions and elaboration

- Their knowledge of bullying and harassment.

The investigation may result in the complaint being upheld or not upheld, or in a decision that the complaint was malicious.

If the complaint is upheld, the decision-maker will consider a range of options:

- Disciplinary action

- Non-disciplinary action

- Counselling, training and/or support for respondent.

If the complaint is not upheld:

- If appropriate, the transfer request of the complainant should be facilitated.

- It should be made clear that any victimisation of the complainant as a result of the complaint will not be tolerated.

If the complaint was malicious:

- It will be viewed as serious misconduct.

- Disciplinary action may be taken.

An appeals procedure must be available to both the alleged perpetrator and the complainant.

Violence and Aggression in the Workplace

Definition

The HSA defines workplace violence and aggression as events in which 'persons are verbally abused, threatened or assaulted in circumstances related to their work' and it is a key health and safety challenge for a lot of organisations, particularly those that have face-to-face contact with the public.

Workplace violence and aggression can range from low-level intimidation, through a medium level of aggression, to a high level of aggression that can lead to violent behaviour. Violence and aggression can come from those outside the organisation, such as members of the public, or from those within the organisation, for example colleagues.

The sectors most at risk are public administration and defence; health and social work; transport, storage and communication; and financial and retail services.

Effects

The effects of violence and aggression on a person can range from the immediate effects of shock and upset to more long-term psychological effects such as lower self-esteem, anxiety, depression and, in more serious cases, post-traumatic stress disorder (PTSD). There can also be knock-on effects on an organisation, including lower morale, difficulty in recruiting and retaining staff, and increased costs due to absenteeism, employer's liability premiums and compensation.

Minimising the Risk

We'll never completely eliminate the risk of violence and aggression occurring in the workplace, but there are ways of reducing the likelihood of it occurring and minimising the consequences. Organisations must carry out a risk assessment in relation to the risk of violence and aggression for their staff. The starting point for this is to determine if there is a problem in relation to violence and aggression and, if so, the extent of that problem. This can be done using various methods including analysing incident reports, talking to staff, issuing questionnaires, learning from similar organisations and trying to predict what might happen.

Unfortunately, a lot of organisations don't have an effective incident reporting procedure and therefore a lot of incidents may go unreported; which means that an organisation may not be aware of the true extent of the problem. Employees can be reluctant to report incidents because they sometimes feel that they reflect badly on them. It is therefore important that employees are encouraged to report and that there is a no-blame environment in place.

The next step in the risk assessment process is to identify who might be harmed. Staff who deal directly with the public, are involved in enforcement duties or are involved in handling cash are examples of more vulnerable groups.

Control measures must then be looked at to ensure that the risk is adequately managed. Control measures will vary from organisation to organisation, but some examples are as follows:

- Policies and procedures in relation to violence and aggression
- Raising awareness among staff and providing training
- Panic buttons, personal alarms and mobile phones
- Check-in system and diary logs for staff working off-site
- Providing screens, wide counters, queuing systems, a relaxing environment in waiting rooms and good layout of interview rooms
- Security staff and CCTV cameras
- Signage stating the organisation's policy in relation to violence and aggression towards staff
- Two-person site visits in certain circumstances.

Staff who are at risk from violence and aggression should be provided with basic training in dealing with such incidents. This should include defusion techniques when faced with difficult situations, as well as the importance of recording and reporting incidents.

Vulnerable Groups

Pregnant, Post-natal and Breastfeeding Employees

Legislation

Part 6, Chapter 2 of the Safety, Health and Welfare at Work (General Application) Regulations 2007 is titled 'Protection of Pregnant, Post Natal and Breastfeeding Employees'.

The regulations apply when an employee informs her employer that she is pregnant and provides an appropriate medical certificate of her condition.

As the earliest stages of pregnancy are the most critical ones for the developing child, it is in the employee's interest to let her employer know she is pregnant as soon as possible.

In these regulations:

- 'Employee' means a pregnant employee, an employee who is breastfeeding or a post-natal employee

- 'Employee who is breastfeeding' means an employee who, having given birth not more than 26 weeks previously, is breastfeeding;

- 'Post-natal employee' means an employee who gave birth not more than 14 weeks preceding a material date.

Employer's Duties

On receiving notification that an employee is pregnant, an employer must assess the specific risks to that employee and take action to ensure that she is not exposed to anything in the workplace that will damage either her safety or health or that of her developing child.

The risk assessment must consider the following:

1. **General hazards:**

    *   physical shocks, including direct blows to the abdomen
    *   vibration – of whole body
    *   handling a load
    *   noise
    *   excessive heat and cold
    *   movement and postures which are abrupt or severe or give rise to excessive fatigue
    *   ionising radiation
    *   non-ionising radiation
    *   certain biological agents, including viruses, bacteria, etc.
    *   certain chemicals, including substances which cause cancer, mercury, anti-cancer drugs and carbon monoxide
    *   underground mine work.

2. **Hazards specific to pregnancy.** Unless the risk assessment indicates that there will be no risk to the safety or health of the employee or the developing child, pregnant employees must not work with/on:

    *   pressurisation chambers
    *   *Rubella*
    *   *Toxoplasma*
    *   lead and lead substances

- underground mine work.

3. **Hazards specific to breastfeeding.** Unless the risk assessment indicates that there will be no risk to the safety or health of the employee or the developing child, employees who are breastfeeding must not work with/on:

   - lead and lead substances

   - underground mine work.

Having completed the risk assessment, the employer must then 'take the preventive and protective measures necessary to ensure the safety and health of such employees and avoid any possible effect on such pregnancy or breastfeeding'.

Where there is risk, and appropriate protective or preventive measures cannot be implemented, the employer must assess if there are any practical ways of avoiding the risk by following these three steps:

1. Adjust the working conditions and/or hours of work. If this does not remove the risk:

2. Provide suitable alternative work. If that is not possible:

3. The employer should assist the employee in receiving health and safety leave under Section 18 of the Maternity Protection Act 1994.

If an employee has a medical certificate stating that for health and safety reasons she should not perform night work during the pregnancy or for 14 weeks afterwards, the employer must remove her from night work by either transferring her to daytime duties or, if this is not feasible, granting her leave. In these circumstances the employee may have an entitlement to health and safety leave under the maternity protection legislation.

The employer is required to give the employee and/or the safety representative information about the outcome of the risk assessment and any measures to be taken.

Employees with Disabilities

Legislation

The Safety, Health and Welfare at Work Act 2005 states that employers must 'ensure, as far as is reasonably practicable, the safety, health and welfare at work of all employees'.

Regulation 25 of the General Application Regulations – Employees with Disabilities states that 'An employer shall ensure that places of work, where necessary, are organised to take account of persons at work with disabilities, in particular as regards doors, passageways, staircases, showers, washbasins, lavatories and workstations used or occupied directly by those persons.'

Under the Employment Equality Acts 1998 and 2004, employers are obliged to take appropriate measures – 'reasonable accommodation'–(unless the costs of doing so are disproportionate) to enable people with disabilities to have access to employment, to participate or advance in employment and to undergo training. Such measures may include training resources or adaptations to:

- workplace premises to make them more accessible for employees with disabilities
- work equipment
- patterns of working time
- distribution of tasks.

Employer's Duties

The company's risk assessments should take account of any particular risks for employees with disabilities and identify whether there are any particular hazards or risks for staff members with conditions such as:

- restricted mobility
- limited dexterity
- impaired vision
- impaired hearing
- limited understanding
- health conditions such as heart problems, epilepsy or asthma.

Employers should consult with employees and with organisations that provide services for people with disabilities to help develop and implement safety procedures and control measures.

Children and Young Persons

Legislation

Part 6, Chapter 1 of the Safety Health and Welfare at Work (General Application) Regulations 2007 is titled 'Protection of Children and Young Persons'.

In these regulations:

- 'child' means a person under 16 years of age
- 'young person' means a person who has reached 16 years of age but is less than 18 years of age.

Employment law restricts the hours that children and young persons may work. The working hours depend on their age, whether it is school term time, etc.:

- A 14-year-old cannot work during school term time, but can work for a maximum of 7 hours per day during school holidays provided those hours are between 8 a.m. and 8 p.m.

- A 15-year-old can work for a total of 8 hours per week during school term time, and can work for a maximum of 7 hours per day during school holidays, provided those hours are between 8 a.m. and 8 p.m.

- 16- and 17-year-olds can work 8 hours per day, and for a total of 40 hours per week, but those hours must be between 6 a.m. and 10 p.m.

Duties

The employer is required to carry out a risk assessment prior to a child or a young person commencing employment. The risk assessment must consider their lack of experience, absence of awareness of existing or potential risks, or lack of maturity.

The risk arising from exposure to specified physical, biological and chemical agents plus specified processes and work must be assessed. These include:

- Ionising radiation
- Work in pressurisation chambers
- Certain biological agents, including viruses, bacteria, etc.
- Certain chemicals, including substances which are toxic or cause cancer

- Work processes referred to in the Safety, Health and Welfare at Work (Carcinogens) Regulations 2001

- Manufacture and handling of devices, fireworks or other objects containing explosives.

The employer must inform the child or young person of any risks identified by the risk assessment and of any control measures to prevent and protect them from any risk. In the case of a child, the employer is also required to inform the parent or guardian.

The employer must not employ a child or young person if the safety and health of that child or young person would be put at risk because the work: is overly physical; may psychologically affect them; exposes them to any agent, such as toxins, carcinogens or radiation; places them at undue risk of accidents because of their inexperience; or exposes them to risk of extreme heat, cold, noise or vibration.

Where the risk assessment reveals a safety or health risk or a risk to the physical or mental development of a child or young person, the employer is required to provide any necessary health surveillance.

Safety Signs in the Workplace

Frequently Asked Questions

When must safety signs be used?

Safety signs must be used whenever a hazard or danger cannot be avoided adequately or reduced in another way. Before installing safety signs an employer should examine whether the hazard can be avoided or reduced by collective precautions (precautions that protect everybody) or safer ways of doing the work.

What regulations apply to safety signs?

The Safety, Health and Welfare at Work (General Application) Regulations 2007 (Chapter 1 of Part 7: Safety Signs at Places of Work) apply to safety signs.

What types of safety signs are there?

A safety sign provides information about safety or health and can be a signboard, colour, acoustic signal, verbal communication, or hand signal.

What is a signboard?

A signboard is a sign that provides information or instruction using a combination of shape, colour and symbols but excludes information in writing.

Why must safety signboards not contain text?

This is because the symbols or pictograms on a signboard are intended to be understood whatever the language ability of the worker viewing it.

How will workers understand the meaning of safety signs?

Employers must provide information to employees on the meaning and requirements of any signs used in the workplace, especially where text on supplementary signboards is used.

Can any text be included on a safety sign?

No. Text may be included on a supplementary signboard provided that it does not adversely affect the effectiveness of the safety signboard.

What colours and shapes should be used on safety signboards?

- Red for prohibition

- Yellow for caution

- Green for positive action

- Blue for mandatory actions

- Discs for prohibitions and instructions

- Triangles for warnings

- Squares and rectangles for emergency and information signs

Examples of Prohibition Signs

Examples of Mandatory Signs

Examples of Warning Signs

HSA 2010 (www.hsa.ie/eng/FAQs/Safety_Signs/)

Index

Health and Safety Authority (*contd*)
roles, 5–6
violence and agression, 154–6
health surveillance scheme, 21
hearing, 76, 81
see also noise
heat regulation, 49, 82–3
HSA (Health and Safety Authority) see
Health and Safety Authority (HSA)
humidity, 84–5

ill health, 7–8, 33, 96–100
see also diseases; infection control
incidents
definition, 33
investigations, 96–100
reference resources, 56
sample report form, 122–8
Industrial Relations Act 1990, 150
infection control, 88–91
see also diseases; ill health
inspections, 31, 94, 95–6, 102–3,
134–6
intoxicants, 5, 67
see also drink
intranet, 24–5
irritants, 139, 145
isolation valves, 130, 133

kitchens, 130, 132

labelling, dangerous substances, 64,
137
legislation
auditor knowledge, 104
CLP (Classification, Labelling and
Packaging) Regulations, 63–4,
66, 136, 137–43

compliance with, 28–9
Control of Vibration at Work
Regulations, 82
CPL (Classification, Packaging and
Labelling) Regulations, 63–4,
66, 136, 143–7
Employment Equality Act 1998,
149, 150, 160
European Communities (Machinery)
Regulations 2008, 59–60
General Application Regulations –
Employees with Disabilities, 160
Guidance in the Display Screen
Equipment Regulations, 85
Industrial Relations Act 1990, 150
Machinery Directive (2006/42/EC),
59–60
Maternity Protection Act 1994, 159
Non-Fatal Offences against the
Person Act 1997, 150
REACH (Registration, Evaluation,
Authorisation and Restriction of
Chemicals) Regulation, 64–5
Safety, Health and Welfare at Work
Act 2005 *see* Safety, Health and
Welfare at Work Act 2005
Safety, Health and Welfare at
Work Act (General Application)
Regulations 2007 *see* Safety,
Health and Welfare at Work
Act (General Application)
Regulations 2007
Safety, Health and Welfare at
Work (General Application)
Regulations 1993, 45, 57
Use of Work Equipment Directive, 59
see also Health and Safety Authority
(HSA)